Learn

Eureka Math®
Grade 2
Module 8

TEKS EDITION

Great Minds® is the creator of *Eureka Math*®, *Wit & Wisdom*®, *Alexandria Plan*™, and *PhD Science*®.

Published by Great Minds PBC.
greatminds.org

Copyright © 2021 Great Minds PBC. Except where otherwise noted, this content is published under a limited public license with the Texas Education Agency. Use limited to Non-Commercial educational purposes. For more information, visit https://gm.greatminds.org/texas.

Printed in the USA
1 2 3 4 5 6 7 8 9 10 CCR 25 24 23 22 21

ISBN 978-1-64929-644-3

Learn ♦ Practice ♦ Succeed

Eureka Math® student materials for *A Story of Units*® (K–5) are available in the *Learn, Practice, Succeed* trio. This series supports differentiation and remediation while keeping student materials organized and accessible. Educators will find that the *Learn, Practice,* and *Succeed* series also offers coherent—and therefore, more effective—resources for Response to Intervention (RTI), extra practice, and summer learning.

Learn

Eureka Math Learn serves as a student's in-class companion where they show their thinking, share what they know, and watch their knowledge build every day. *Learn* assembles the daily classwork—Application Problems, Exit Tickets, Problem Sets, templates—in an easily stored and navigated volume.

Practice

Each *Eureka Math* lesson begins with a series of energetic, joyous fluency activities, including those found in *Eureka Math Practice*. Students who are fluent in their math facts can master more material more deeply. With *Practice,* students build competence in newly acquired skills and reinforce previous learning in preparation for the next lesson.

Together, *Learn* and *Practice* provide all the print materials students will use for their core math instruction.

Succeed

Eureka Math Succeed enables students to work individually toward mastery. These additional problem sets align lesson by lesson with classroom instruction, making them ideal for use as homework or extra practice. Each problem set is accompanied by a Homework Helper, a set of worked examples that illustrate how to solve similar problems.

Teachers and tutors can use *Succeed* books from prior grade levels as curriculum-consistent tools for filling gaps in foundational knowledge. Students will thrive and progress more quickly as familiar models facilitate connections to their current grade-level content.

Students, families, and educators:

Thank you for being part of the *Eureka Math*® community, where we celebrate the joy, wonder, and thrill of mathematics.

In the *Eureka Math* classroom, new learning is activated through rich experiences and dialogue. The *Learn* book puts in each student's hands the prompts and problem sequences they need to express and consolidate their learning in class.

What is in the Learn book?

Application Problems: Problem solving in a real-world context is a daily part of *Eureka Math*. Students build confidence and perseverance as they apply their knowledge in new and varied situations. The curriculum encourages students to use the RDW process—Read the problem, Draw to make sense of the problem, and Write an equation and a solution. Teachers facilitate as students share their work and explain their solution strategies to one another.

Problem Sets: A carefully sequenced Problem Set provides an in-class opportunity for independent work, with multiple entry points for differentiation. Teachers can use the Preparation and Customization process to select "Must Do" problems for each student. Some students will complete more problems than others; what is important is that all students have a 10-minute period to immediately exercise what they've learned, with light support from their teacher.

Students bring the Problem Set with them to the culminating point of each lesson: the Student Debrief. Here, students reflect with their peers and their teacher, articulating and consolidating what they wondered, noticed, and learned that day.

Exit Tickets: Students show their teacher what they know through their work on the daily Exit Ticket. This check for understanding provides the teacher with valuable real-time evidence of the efficacy of that day's instruction, giving critical insight into where to focus next.

Templates: From time to time, the Application Problem, Problem Set, or other classroom activity requires that students have their own copy of a picture, reusable model, or data set. Each of these templates is provided with the first lesson that requires it.

Where can I learn more about *Eureka Math* resources?

The Great Minds® team is committed to supporting students, families, and educators with an ever-growing library of resources, available at eureka-math.org. The website also offers inspiring stories of success in the *Eureka Math* community. Share your insights and accomplishments with fellow users by becoming a *Eureka Math* Champion.

Best wishes for a year filled with aha moments!

Jill Diniz
Director of Mathematics
Great Minds

The Read–Draw–Write Process

The *Eureka Math* curriculum supports students as they problem-solve by using a simple, repeatable process introduced by the teacher. The Read–Draw–Write (RDW) process calls for students to

1. Read the problem.
2. Draw and label.
3. Write an equation.
4. Write a word sentence (statement).

Educators are encouraged to scaffold the process by interjecting questions such as

- What do you see?
- Can you draw something?
- What conclusions can you make from your drawing?

The more students participate in reasoning through problems with this systematic, open approach, the more they internalize the thought process and apply it instinctively for years to come.

Contents

Module 8: Time, Shapes, and Fractions as Equal Parts of Shapes

Topic A: Attributes of Geometric Shapes
Lesson 1 1
Lesson 2 7
Lesson 3 15
Lesson 4 21
Lesson 5 27

Topic B: Composite Shapes and Fraction Concepts
Lesson 6 33
Lesson 7 41
Lesson 8 47

Topic C: Fractions of Circles and Rectangles
Lesson 9 53
Lesson 10 63
Lesson 11 71

Topic D: Application of Fractions to Tell Time
Lesson 12 77
Lesson 13 81
Lesson 14 87
Lesson 15 101
Lesson 16 111

R (Read the problem carefully.)

Terrence is making shapes with 12 toothpicks. Using all of the toothpicks, create 3 different shapes he could make. How many other combinations can you find?

D (Draw a picture.)

A STORY OF UNITS – TEKS EDITION

Lesson 1 Problem Set 2•8

Name _____ Date _____

1. Identify the number of sides, angles, and vertices for each shape. The first one has been done for you.

a.

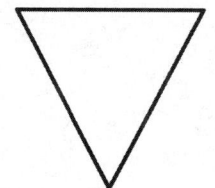

__3__ sides

__3__ angles

__3__ vertices

b.

_____ sides

_____ angles

_____ vertices

c.

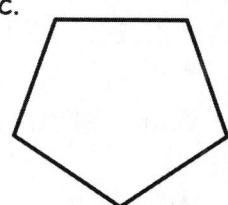

_____ sides

_____ angles

_____ vertices

d.

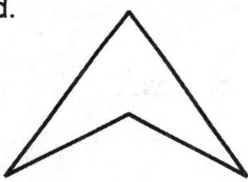

_____ sides

_____ angles

_____ vertices

e.

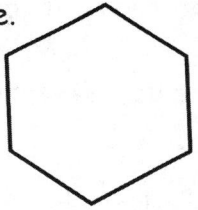

_____ sides

_____ angles

_____ vertices

f.

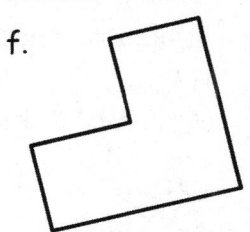

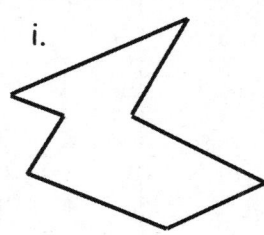

_____ sides

_____ angles

_____ vertices

g.

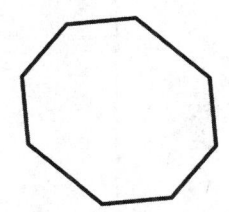

_____ sides

_____ angles

_____ vertices

h.

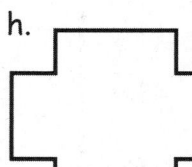

_____ sides

_____ angles

_____ vertices

i.

_____ sides

_____ angles

_____ vertices

Lesson 1:   Describe two-dimensional shapes based on attributes.

A STORY OF UNITS – TEKS EDITION   Lesson 1 Problem Set 2•8

2. Study the shapes below. Then, answer the questions.

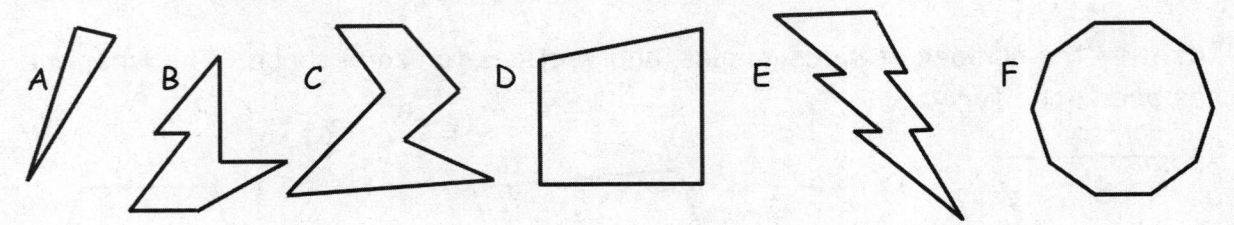

   A   B   C   D   E   F

   a. Which shape has the most sides? _____

   b. Which shape has 3 more angles than shape C? _____

   c. Which shape has 3 fewer sides than shape B? _____

   d. How many more angles does shape C have than shape A? _____

   e. Which of these shapes have the same number of sides and angles? _____

   f. Which of these shapes have the same number of angles and vertices?

3. Ethan said the two shapes below are both hexagons, but just different sizes. Explain why he is incorrect.

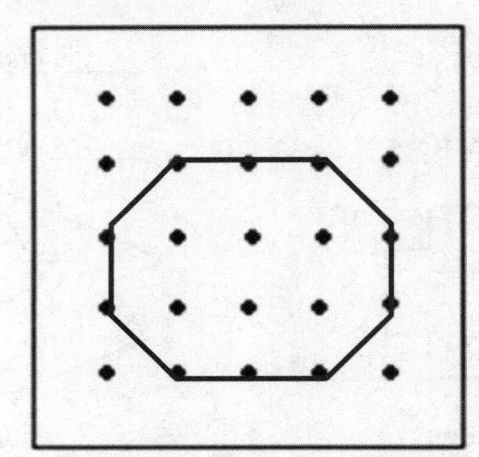

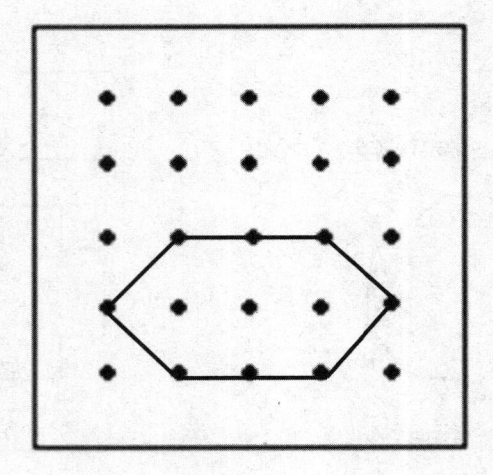

_____

_____

Lesson 1:   Describe two-dimensional shapes based on attributes.

A STORY OF UNITS – TEKS EDITION　　　　　　　　　　Lesson 1 Exit Ticket　2•8

Name _____   Date _____

Study the shapes below. Then, answer the questions.

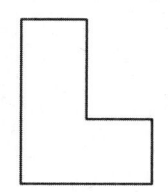

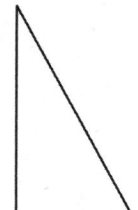

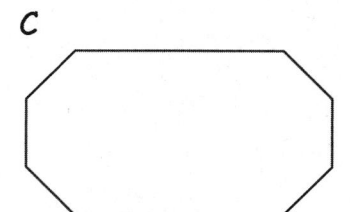

A　　　　　　　B　　　　　　　C　　　　　　　D

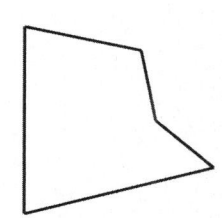

1. Which shape has the most sides? _____

2. Which shape has 3 fewer angles than shape C? _____

3. Which shape has 3 more sides than shape B? _____

4. Which of these shapes have the same number of sides and angles? _____

5. Which of these shapes have the same number of sides and vertices? _____

Lesson 1:　Describe two-dimensional shapes based on attributes.

R (Read the problem carefully.)

How many triangles can you find? (Hint: If you only found 10, keep looking!)

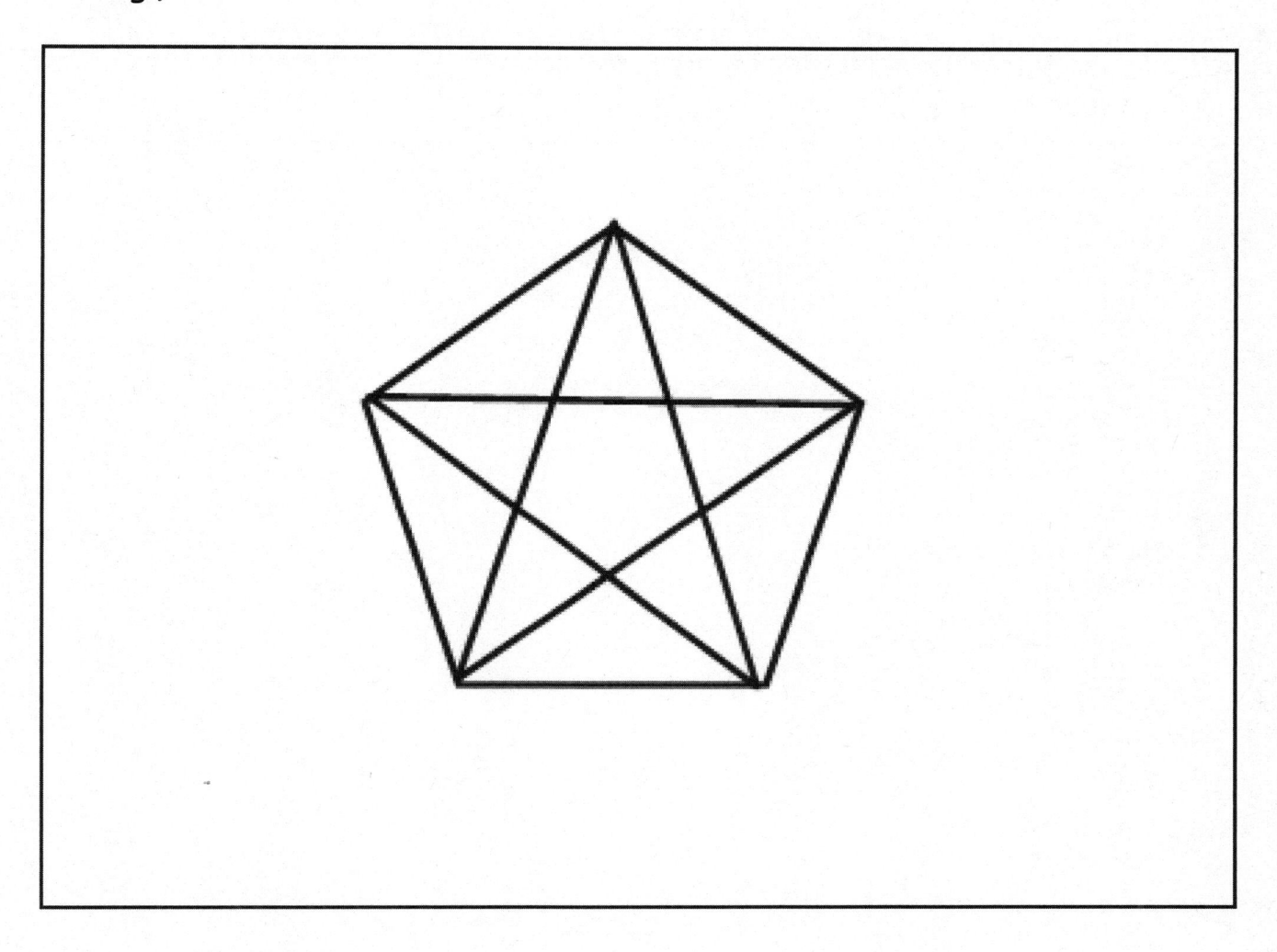

W (Write a Statement that matches the story.)

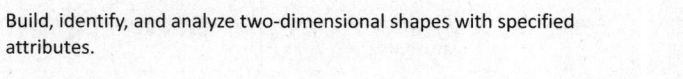

_____

_____

find the triangles

find the triangles

A STORY OF UNITS – TEKS EDITION

Lesson 2 Problem Set 2•8

Name _____ Date _____

1. Count the number of sides and angles for each shape to identify each polygon. The polygon names in the word bank may be used more than once.

Hexagon	Quadrilateral	Triangle	Pentagon
Nonagon	Octagon	Decagon	Heptagon

a. _____

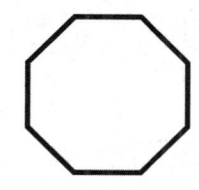

b. _____

c. _____

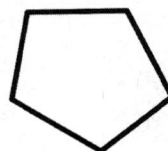

d. _____

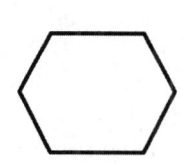

e. _____

f. _____

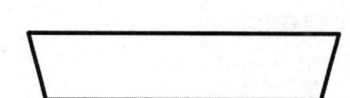

g. _____

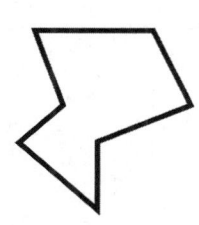

h. _____

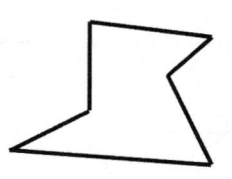

i. _____

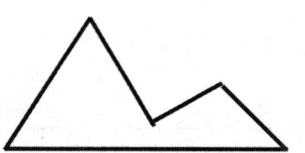

j. _____

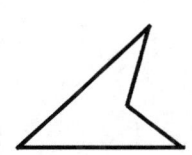

k. _____

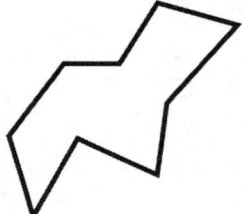

l. _____

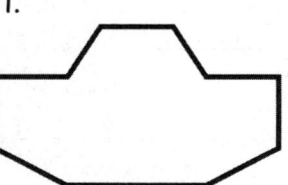

Lesson 2: Build, identify, and analyze two-dimensional shapes with specified attributes.

2. Draw more sides to complete 2 examples of each polygon.

	Example 1	Example 2
a. **Triangle** For each example, _____ line was added. A triangle has _____ total sides.		
b. **Hexagon** For each example, _____ lines were added. A hexagon has _____ total sides.		
c. **Quadrilateral** For each example, _____ lines were added. A quadrilateral has _____ total sides.		
d. **Pentagon** For each example, _____ lines were added. A pentagon has _____ total sides.		

3. a. Explain why both polygons A and B are hexagons.

   _____

   _____

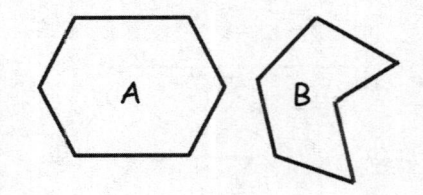

   b. Draw a different hexagon than the two that are shown.

4. Explain why both polygons C and D are quadrilaterals.

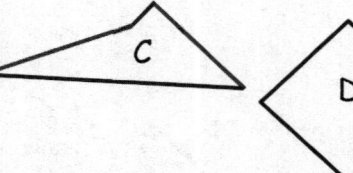

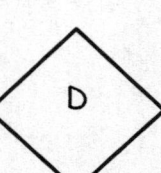

   _____

   _____

Lesson 2: Build, identify, and analyze two-dimensional shapes with specified attributes.

Name _____ Date _____

Count the number of sides and angles for each shape to identify each polygon. The polygon names in the word bank may be used more than once.

| Hexagon   Quadrilateral   Triangle   Pentagon |

1. _____

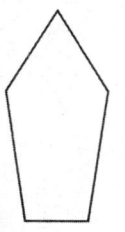

2. _____

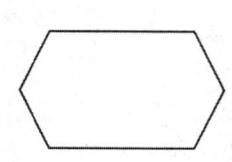

3. _____

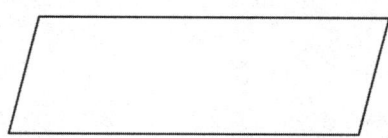

4. _____

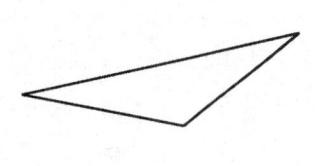

5. _____

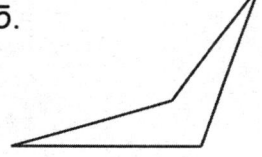

6. _____

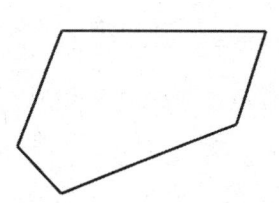

R (Read the problem carefully.)

Three sides of a quadrilateral have the following lengths: 19 cm, 23 cm, and 26 cm. If the total distance around the shape is 86 cm, what is the length of the fourth side?

D (Draw a picture.)

W (Write and solve an equation.)

W (Write a Statement that matches the story.)

_____

_____

_____

Name _____ Date _____

1. Use a straightedge to draw the polygon with the given attributes in the space to the right.

   a. Draw a polygon with 3 angles.
      Number of sides: _____
      Name of polygon: _____

   b. Draw a five-sided polygon.
      Number of vertices: _____
      Name of polygon: _____

   c. Draw a polygon with 4 angles.
      Number of sides: _____
      Name of polygon: _____

   d. Draw a polygon with six vertices.
      Number of angles: _____
      Name of polygon: _____

   e. Draw a polygon with 8 vertices.
      Number of sides: _____
      Name of polygon: _____

   f. Draw a polygon with 10 angles.
      Number of vertices: _____
      Name of polygon: _____

   g. Draw a 9-sided polygon.
      Number of angles: _____
      Name of polygon: _____

   h. Draw a polygon with 7 vertices.
      Number of angles: _____
      Name of polygon: _____

Lesson 3: Use attributes to draw different polygons including triangles, quadrilaterals, pentagons, and hexagons.

2. Use your straightedge to draw 2 new examples of each polygon that are different from those you drew on the first page.

   a. Triangle

   b. Pentagon

   c. Quadrilateral

   d. Hexagon

A STORY OF UNITS – TEKS EDITION　　　Lesson 3 Exit Ticket　2•8

Name _____   Date _____

Use a straightedge to draw the polygon with the given attributes in the space to the right.

Draw a five-sided polygon.

Number of angles: _____

Name of polygon: _____

Lesson 3: Use attributes to draw different polygons including triangles, quadrilaterals, pentagons, and hexagons.

R (Read the problem carefully.)

Juanita earns $22 walking dogs. She spends $6 on a coloring book and $3 on crayons. Juanita deposits the rest of the money in her bank account. How much money does Juanita deposit?

D (Draw a picture.)

W (Write and solve an equation.)

W (Write a statement that matches the story.)

_____

_____

_____

Name _____ Date _____

1. Use your ruler to draw 2 parallel lines that are not the same length.

2. Use your ruler to draw 2 parallel lines that are the same length.

3. Trace the parallel lines on each quadrilateral using a crayon. For each shape with two sets of parallel lines, use two different colors. Use your index card to find each square angle, and box it.

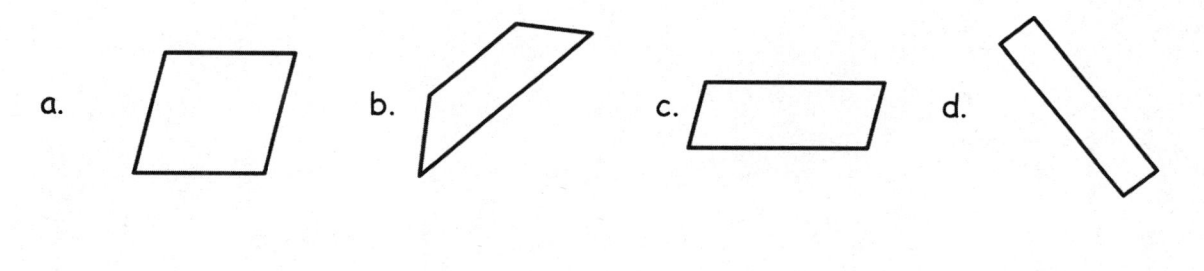

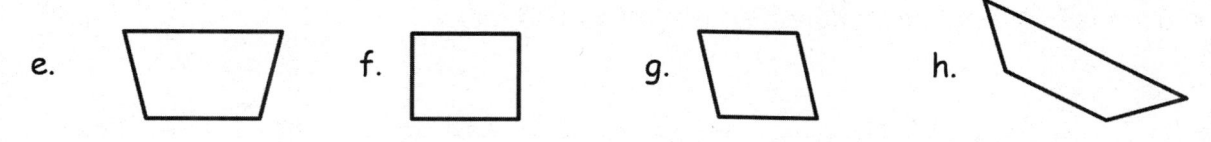

a.   b.   c.   d.

e.   f.   g.   h.

4. Draw a parallelogram with no square angles.

5. Draw a quadrilateral with 4 square angles.

6. Measure and label the sides of the figure to the right with your centimeter ruler. What do you notice? Be ready to talk about the attributes of this quadrilateral. Can you remember what this polygon is called?

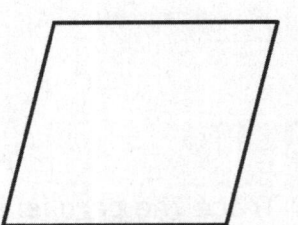

7. A square is a special rectangle. What makes it special?

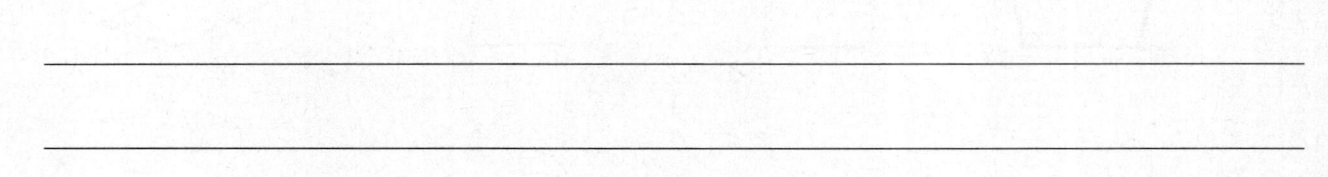

_____

_____

Name _____ Date _____

Use crayons to trace the parallel sides on each quadrilateral. Use your index card to find each square angle, and box it.

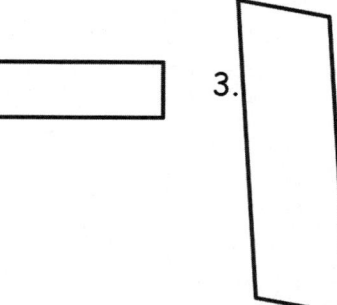

1. 　　　2. 　　　3. 　　　4.

R (Read the problem carefully.)

a. Sort the shapes into three groups that make sense to you.

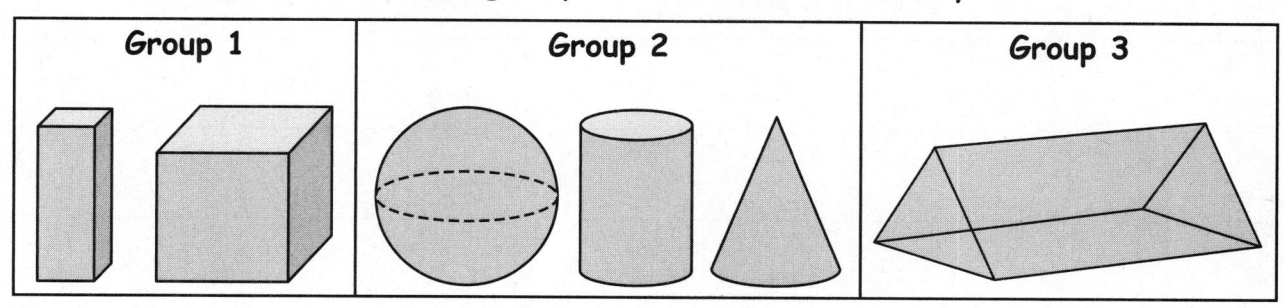

Group 1	Group 2	Group 3

b. Describe how your shapes are sorted.

Group 1	Group 2	Group 3

D (Draw a picture.)

W (Write about your sort.)

_____

_____

_____

Name _____ Date _____

1. Use your geometric solids to complete the table.

Solid Figure	Number of Faces	Shape of Faces	Number of Edges	Number of Vertices
Cube				
Rectangular Prism				
Triangular Prism				
Cone				
Cylinder				
Sphere				

Lesson 5: Classify and sort three-dimensional figures according to their attributes.

2. Sort the geometric solids into three groups using their names. Give each group a title that explains why you grouped the geometric solids together. Be sure to use the words *face*, *edge*, and *vertex*.

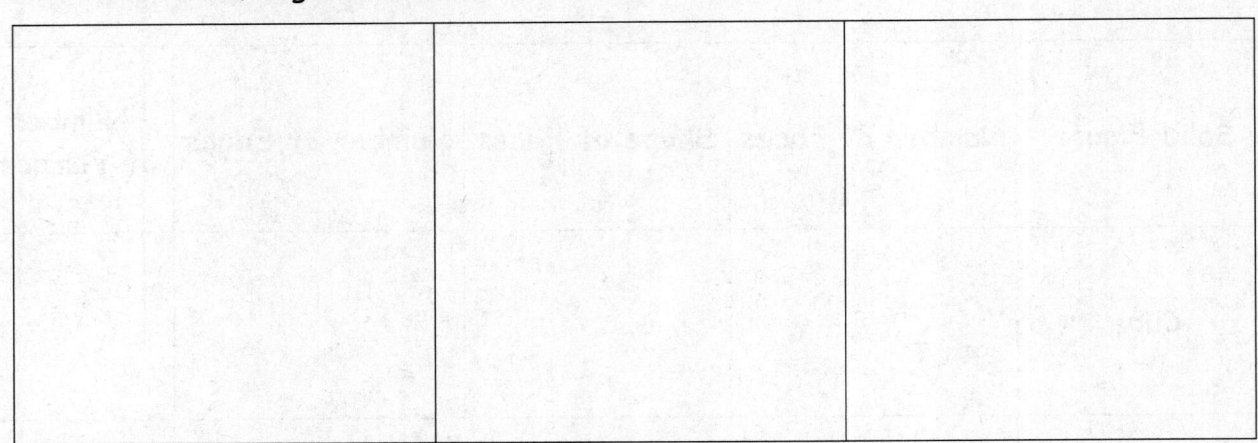

3. Jim drew a cone and labeled it. Explain Jim's mistake.

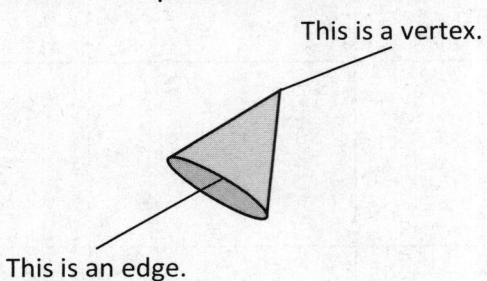

This is a vertex.

This is an edge.

Name _____ Date _____

1. Fill in the blanks to label the characteristics of the rectangular prism.

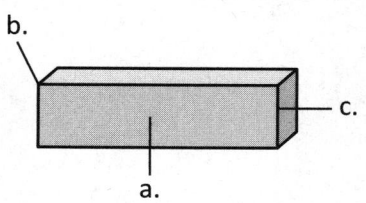

   a. _____

   b. _____

   c. _____

2. Explain why a cylinder is not a prism.

R (Read the problem carefully.)

Frank has 19 fewer cubes than Josie. Frank has 56 cubes. They want to use all of their cubes to build a tower. How many cubes will they use?

D (Draw a picture.)

W (Write and solve an equation.)

W (Write a statement that matches the story.)

_____

_____

Name _____ Date _____

1. Identify each polygon labeled in the tangram as precisely as possible in the space below.

   a. _____

   b. _____

   c. _____

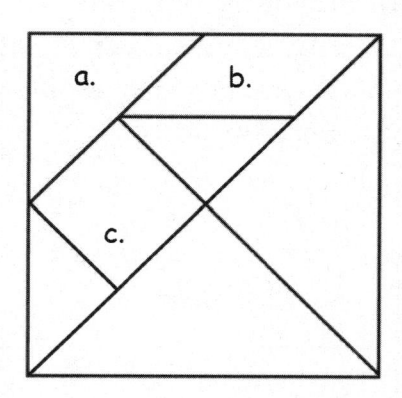

2. Use the square and the two smallest triangles of your tangram pieces to make the following polygons. Draw them in the space provided.

a. A quadrilateral with exactly 1 pair of parallel sides.	b. A quadrilateral with no square angles.
c. A quadrilateral with 4 square angles.	d. A triangle with 1 square angle.

Lesson 6: Combine shapes to create a composite shape; create a new shape from composite shapes.

3. Use the parallelogram and the two smallest triangles of your tangram pieces to make the following polygons. Draw them in the space provided.

a. A quadrilateral with 1 pair of parallel sides.	b. A quadrilateral with no square angles.
c. A quadrilateral with 4 square angles.	d. A triangle with 1 square angle.

4. Rearrange the parallelogram and the two smallest triangles to make a hexagon. Draw the new shape below.

5. Rearrange your tangram pieces to make other polygons! Identify them as you work.

Name _____   Date _____

Use your tangram pieces to make two new polygons. Draw a picture of each new polygon, and name them.

1.

2.

Lesson 6: Combine shapes to create a composite shape; create a new shape from composite shapes.

Cut the tangram into 7 puzzle pieces.

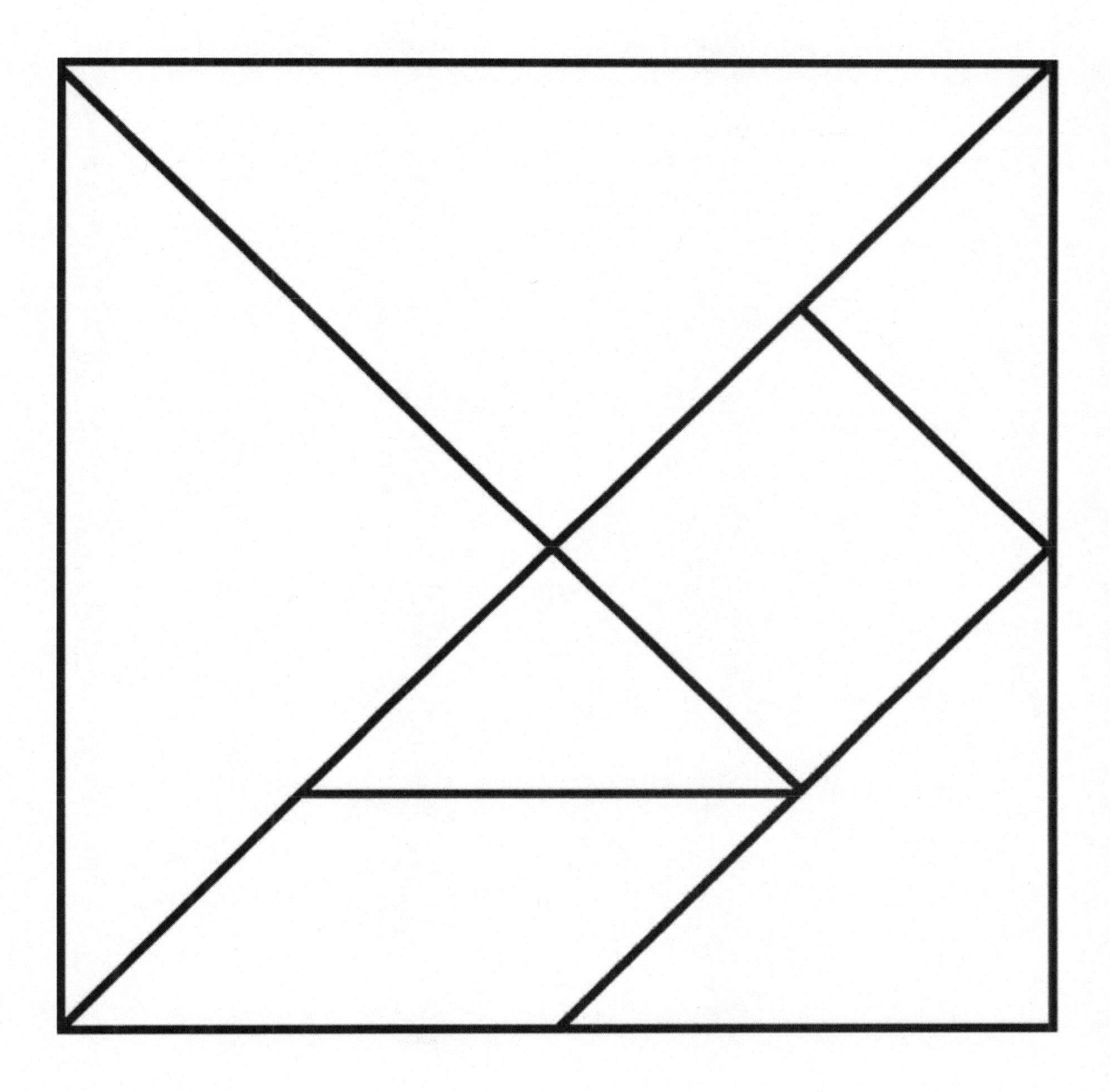

tangram

Lesson 6: Combine shapes to create a composite shape; create a new shape from composite shapes.

R (Read the problem carefully.)

Vishal saves $3 each week. After 7 weeks, how much money does Vishal save?

D (Draw a picture.)

W (Write and solve an equation.)

W (Write a statement that matches the story.)

_____

_____

_____

Name _____ Date _____

1. Solve the following puzzles using your tangram pieces. Draw your solutions in the space below.

a. Use the two smallest triangles to make one larger triangle.	b. Use the two smallest triangles to make a parallelogram with no square corners.
c. Use the two smallest triangles to make a square.	d. Use the two largest triangles to make a square.
e. How many equal shares do the larger shapes in Parts (a–d) have?	f. How many halves make up the larger shapes in Parts (a–d)?

2. Circle the shapes that show halves.

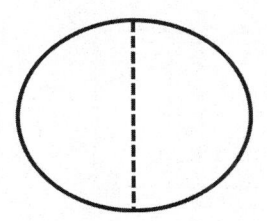

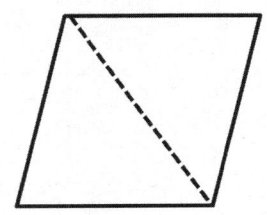

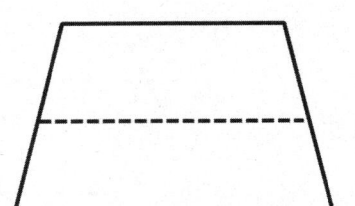

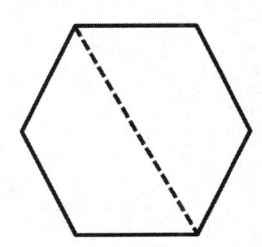

3. Show how 3 triangle pattern blocks form a trapezoid. Draw the shape below.

   a. How many equal shares does the trapezoid have? _____
   b. How many thirds are in the trapezoid? _____

4. Circle the shapes that show thirds.

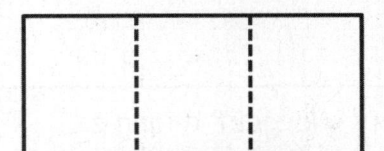

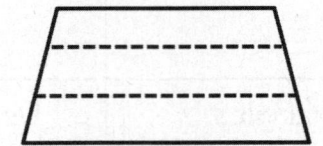

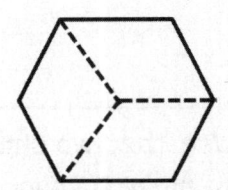

5. Add another triangle to the trapezoid you made in Problem 3 to make a parallelogram. Draw the new shape below.

   a. How many equal shares does the shape have now? _____
   b. How many fourths are in the shape? _____

6. Circle the shapes that show fourths.

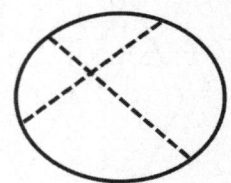

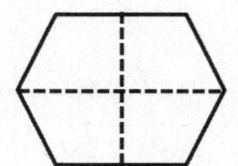

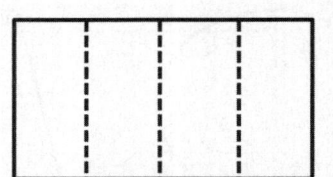

Name _____ Date _____

1. Circle the shapes that show thirds.

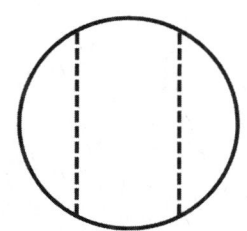

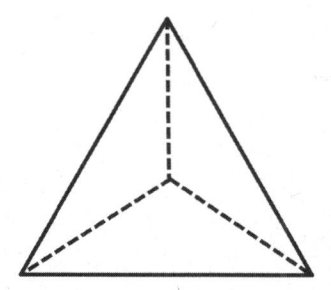

2. Circle the shapes that show fourths.

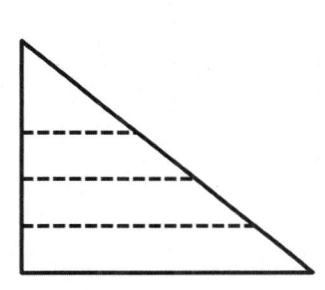

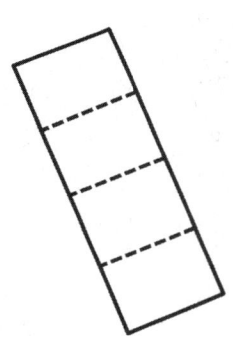

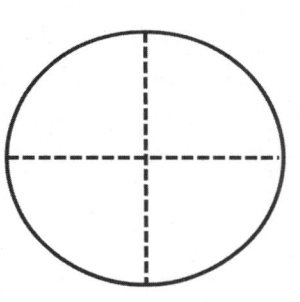

R (Read the problem carefully.)

Students were making larger shapes out of triangles and squares.

They put away all 72 triangles. There were still 48 squares on the carpet.

How many triangles and squares were on the carpet when they started?

D (Draw a picture.)

W (Write and solve an equation.)

W (Write a statement that matches the story.)

_____

_____

_____

Name _____ Date _____

1. Use one pattern block to cover half the rhombus.

   a. Identify the pattern block used to cover half of the rhombus. _____

   b. Draw a picture of the rhombus formed by the 2 halves.

2. Use one pattern block to cover half the hexagon.

   a. Identify the pattern block used to cover half of a hexagon. _____

   b. Draw a picture of the hexagon formed by the 2 halves.

3. Use one pattern block to cover 1 third of the hexagon.

   a. Identify the pattern block used to cover 1 third of a hexagon. _____

   b. Draw a picture of the hexagon formed by the 3 thirds.

4. Use one pattern block to cover 1 third of the trapezoid.

   a. Identify the pattern block used to cover 1 third of a trapezoid. _____

   b. Draw a picture of the trapezoid formed by the 3 thirds.

Lesson 8: Interpret equal shares in composite shapes as halves, thirds, and fourths.

5. Use 4 pattern block squares to make one larger square.

   a. Draw a picture of the square formed in the space below.

   b. Shade 1 small square. Each small square is 1 _____ (half / third / fourth) of the whole square.

   c. Shade 1 more small square. Now, 2 _____ (halves / thirds / fourths) of the whole square is shaded.

   d. And 2 fourths of the square is the same as 1 _____ (half / third / fourth) of the whole square.

   e. Shade 2 more small squares. _____ fourths is equal to 1 whole.

6. Use one pattern block to cover 1 sixth of the hexagon.

   a. Identify the pattern block used to cover 1 sixth of a hexagon. _____

   b. Draw a picture of the hexagon formed by the 6 sixths.

Name _____ Date _____

Name the pattern block used to cover half the rectangle. _____

Use the shape below to draw the pattern blocks used to cover 2 halves.

R (Read the problem carefully.)

Mr. Thompson's class raised 96 dollars for a field trip. They need to raise a total of 120 dollars.

  a. How much more money do they need to raise in order to reach their goal?

  b. If they raise 86 more dollars, how much extra money will they have?

D (Draw a picture.)

W (Write and solve an equation.)

W (Write a statement that matches the story.)

a. _____

_____

b. _____

_____

Name _____   Date _____

1. Circle the shapes that have 2 equal shares with 1 share shaded.

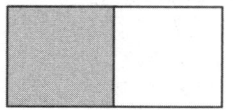

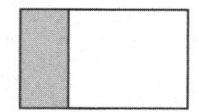

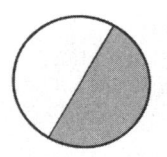

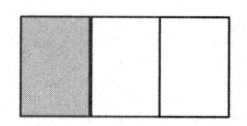

2. Shade 1 half of the shapes that are split into 2 equal shares. One has been done for you.

a.

b.

c.

d.

e.

f.

g.

h.

i.

j.

k.

Lesson 9: Partition circles and rectangles into equal parts, and describe those parts as halves, thirds, or fourths.

3. Partition the shapes to show halves. Shade 1 half of each. Compare your halves to your partner's.

   a.

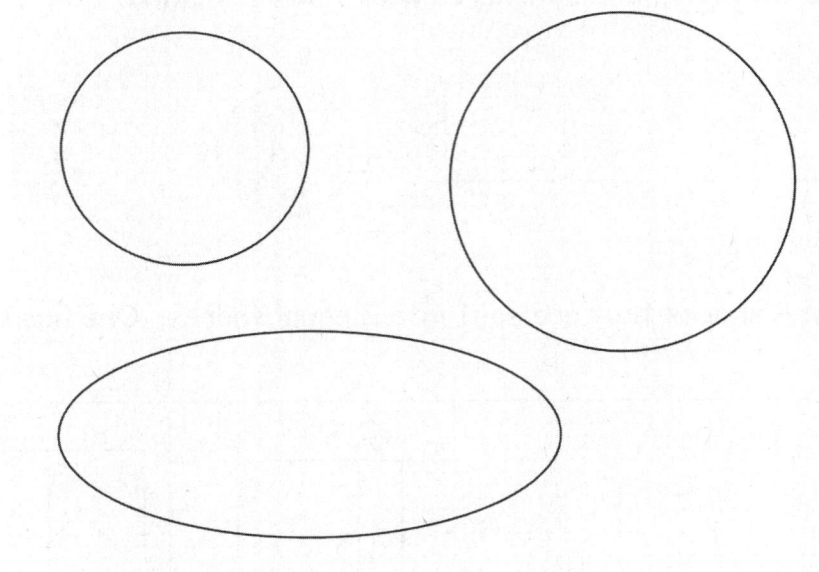

   b.

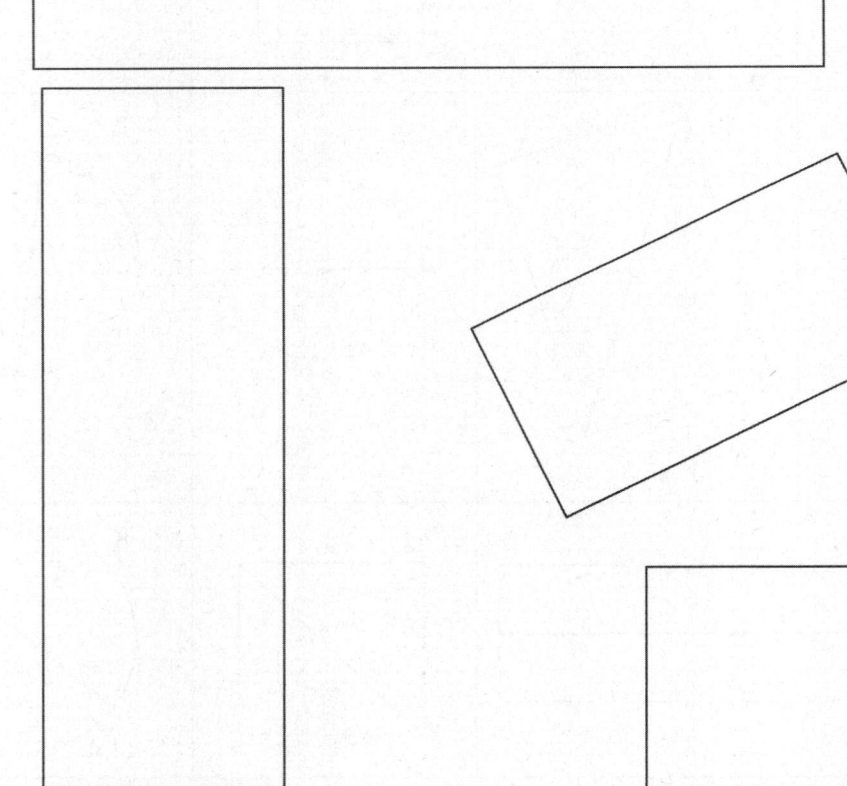

Name _____ Date _____

Shade 1 half of the shapes that are split into 2 equal shares.

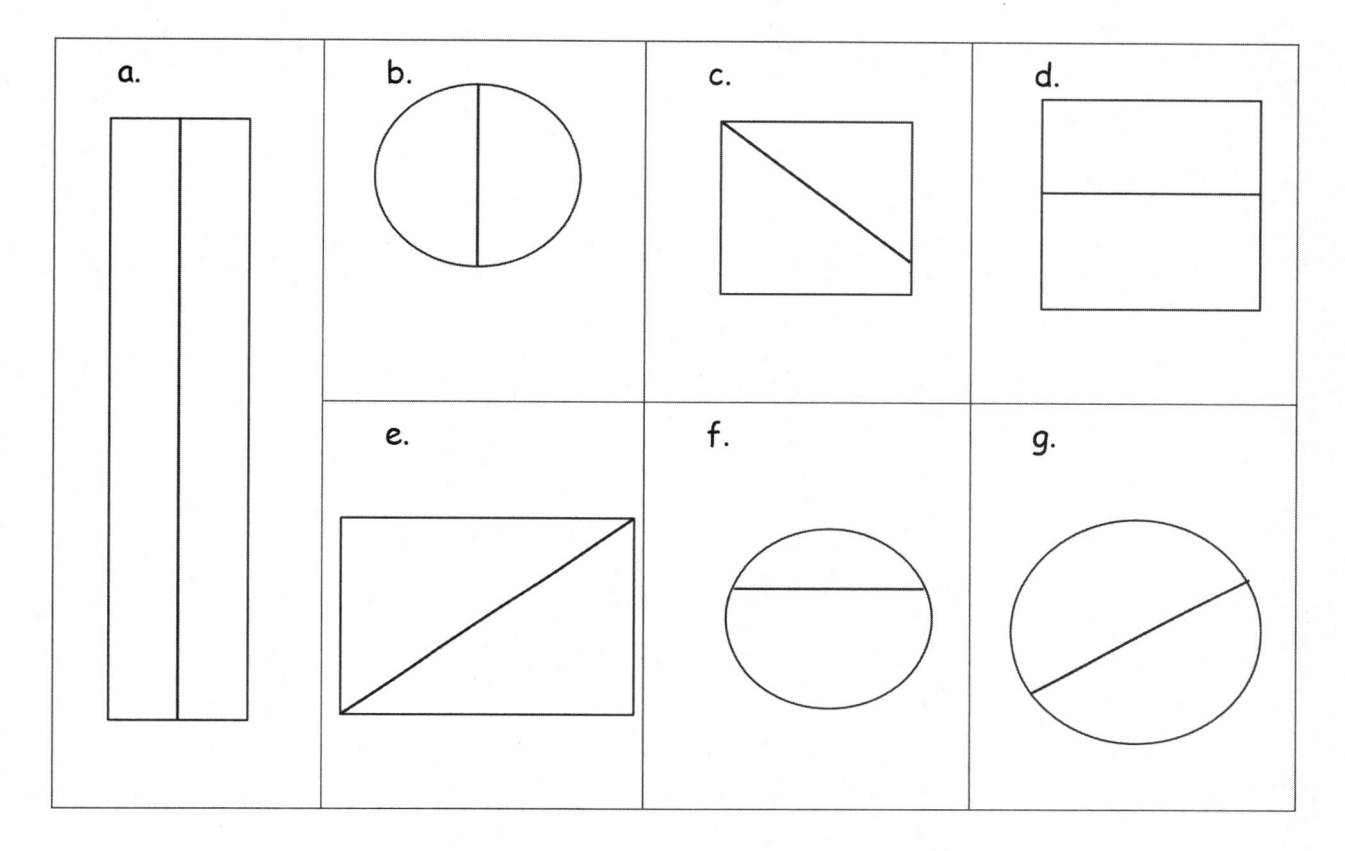

| a. | b. | c. | d. |
| e. | f. | g. | |

Lesson 9: Partition circles and rectangles into equal parts, and describe those parts as halves, thirds, or fourths.

_____

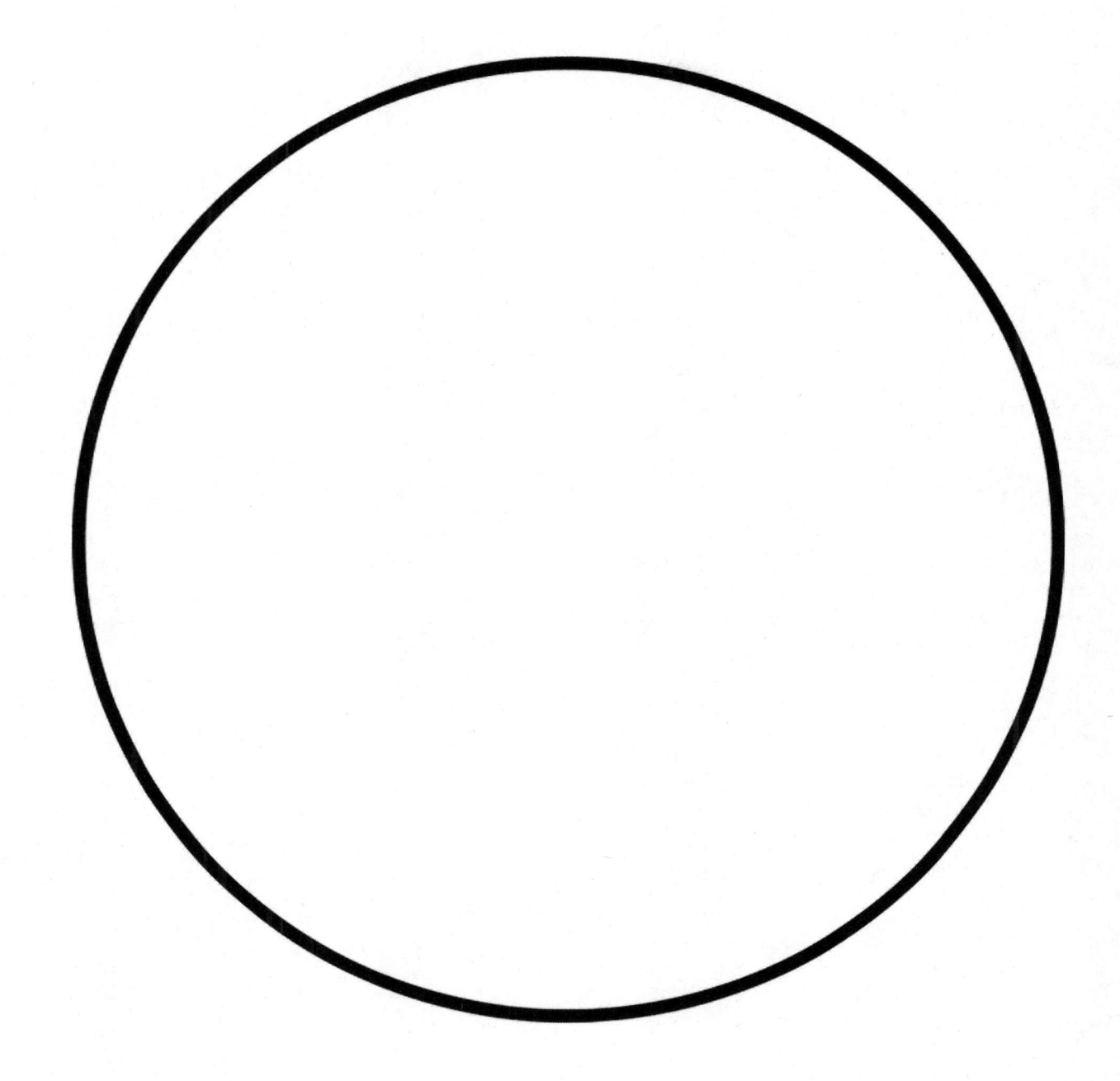

circle

Lesson 9: Partition circles and rectangles into equal parts, and describe those parts as halves, thirds, or fourths.

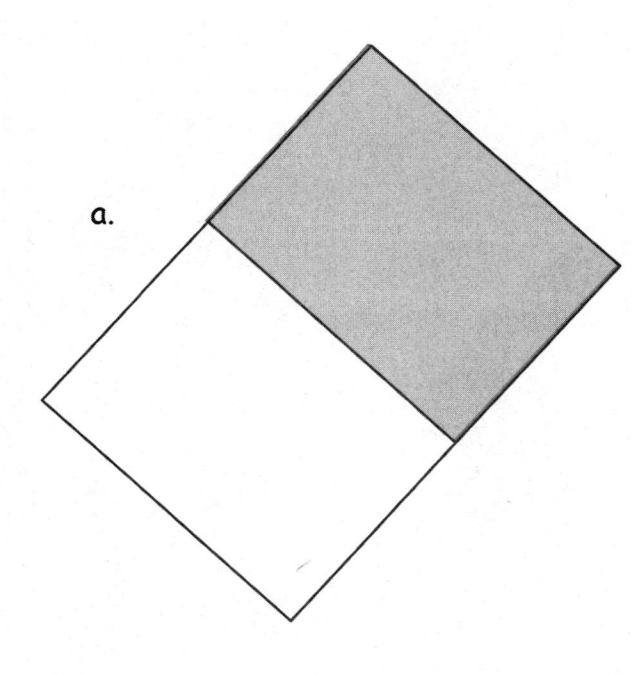

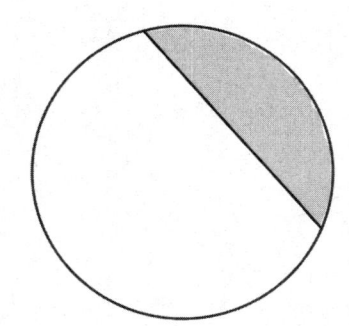

a.

b.

c.

d.

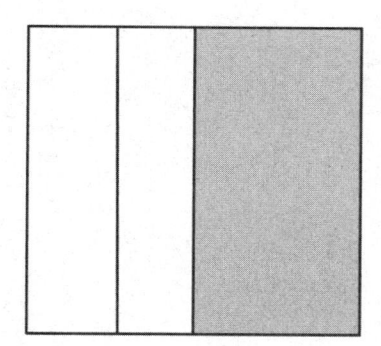

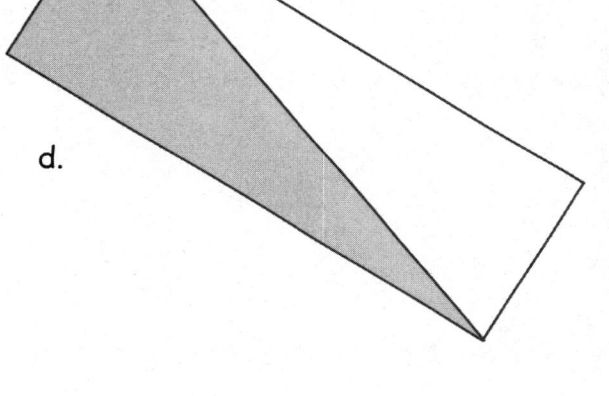

e.

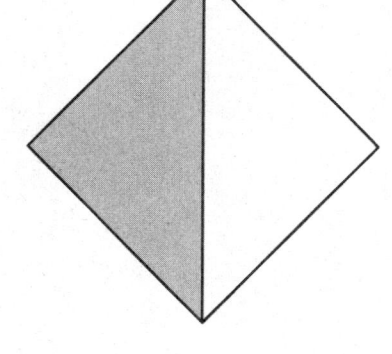

f.

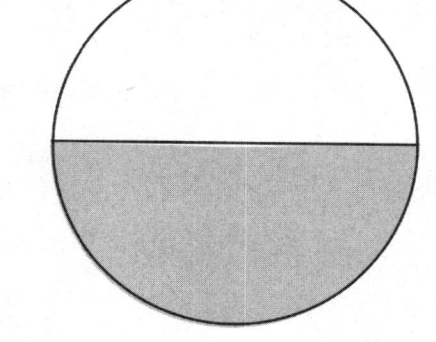

Shaded shapes

R (Read the problem carefully.)

Felix is passing out raffle tickets. He passes out 98 tickets and has 57 left. How many raffle tickets did he have to start?

D (Draw a picture.)

W (Write and solve an equation.)

W (Write a statement that matches the story.)

Name _____ Date _____

1. a. Do the shapes below show halves or thirds? _____

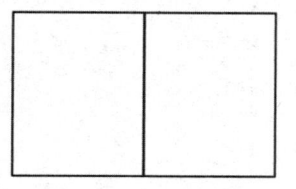

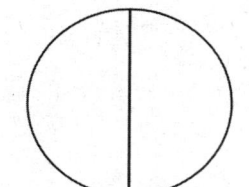

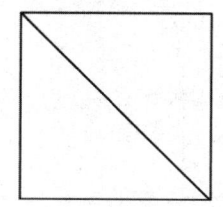

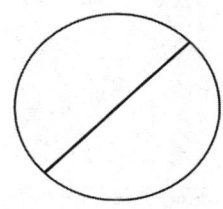

   b. Draw 1 more line to partition each shape above into fourths.

2. Partition each rectangle into eighths. Then, shade the shapes as indicated.

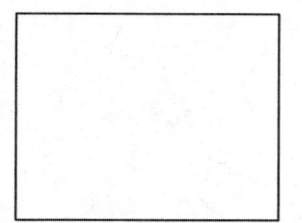

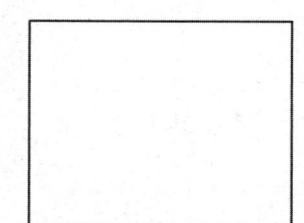

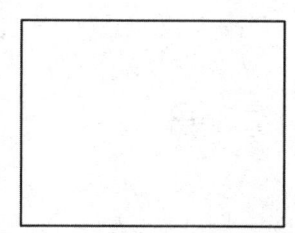

   5 eighths   4 eighths   1 eighth

3. Partition each circle into fourths. Then, shade the shapes as indicated.

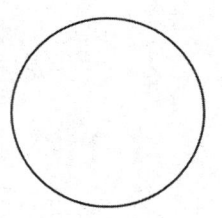

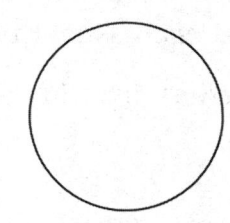

   4 fourths   3 fourths   2 fourths   1 fourth

Lesson 10: Partition circles and rectangles into equal parts, and describe those parts as halves, fourths, and eighths.

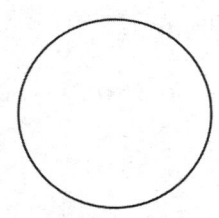

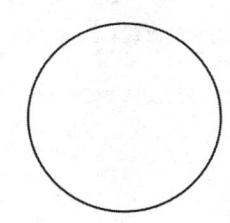

4. Partition and shade the following shapes as indicated. Each rectangle or circle is one whole.

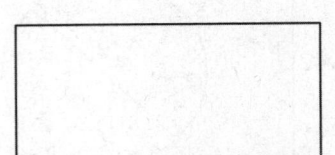

   a. 3 fourths

   b. 1 eighth

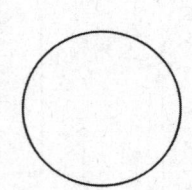

   c. 1 half

   d. 2 fourths

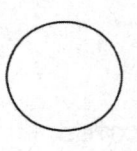

   e. 5 eighths

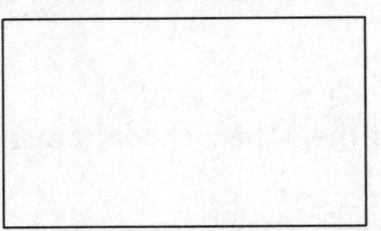

   f. 8 eighths

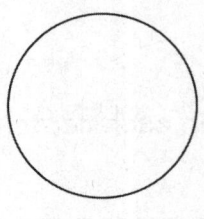

   g. 1 fourth

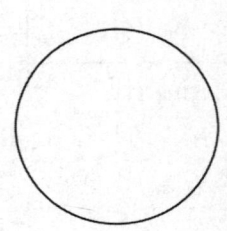

   h. 2 eighths

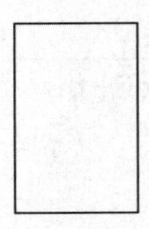

   i. 4 fourths

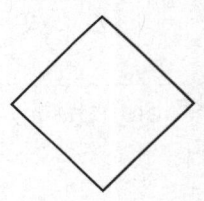

5. Split the pizza below so that Maria, Paul, Jose, and Mark each have an equal share. Label each student's share with his or her name.

   a. What fraction of the pizza was eaten by each of the boys?

   b. What fraction of the pizza did the boys eat altogether?

A STORY OF UNITS – TEKS EDITION

Lesson 10 Exit Ticket 2•8

Name _____ Date _____

Partition and shade the following shapes as indicated. Each rectangle or circle is one whole.

1. 2 halves

2. 1 eighth

3. 3 eighths

4. 1 half

5. 2 fourths

6. 1 fourth

Lesson 10: Partition circles and rectangles into equal parts, and describe those parts as halves, fourths, and eighths.

rectangles and circles

R (Read the problem carefully.)

Jacob collected 70 baseball cards. He gave half of them to his brother, Sammy. How many baseball cards does Jacob have left?

D (Draw a picture.)

W (Write and solve an equation.)

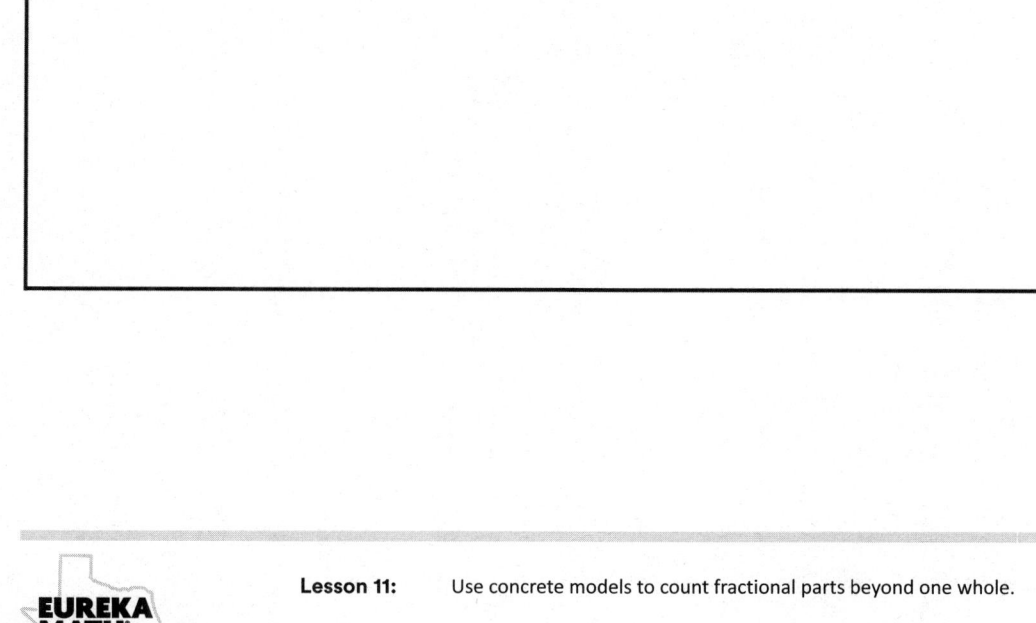

W (Write a statement that matches the story.)

_____

_____

_____

Name _____ Date _____

1. For Parts (a) and (c) identify the shaded area.

   a.

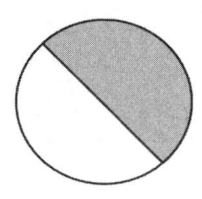

   _____ half 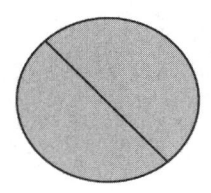   _____ halves

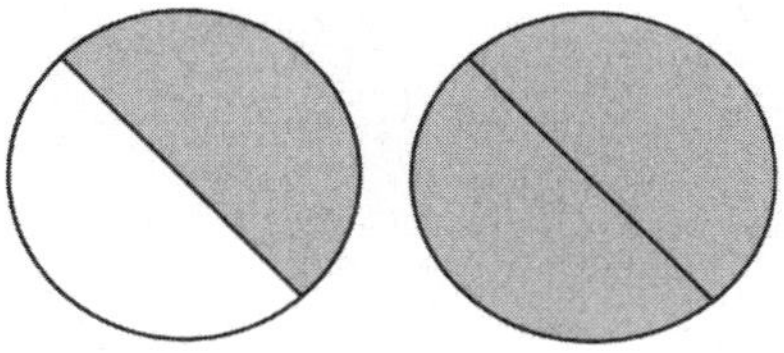

   _____ halves 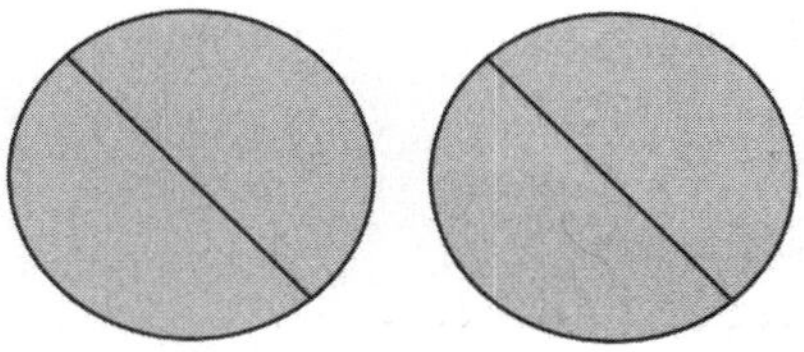   _____ halves

   b. Circle the shape above that has a shaded area that shows 1 whole.

   c.

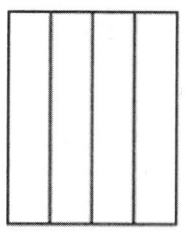

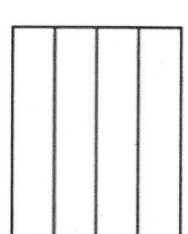

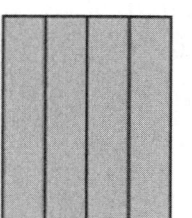

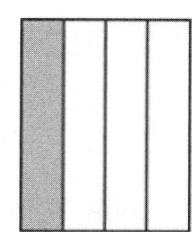

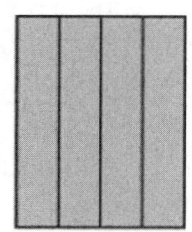

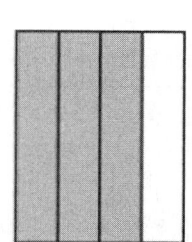

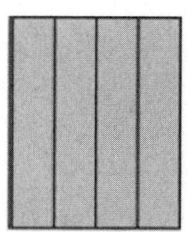

   _____ fourth   _____ fourths   _____ fourths   _____ fourths

   d. Circle the shape above that has a shaded area that shows 1 whole.

Lesson 11: Use concrete models to count fractional parts beyond one whole.

Lesson 11 Problem Set 2•8

2. What fraction do you need to color so that 1 whole is shaded?

a.

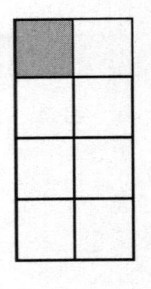

b.

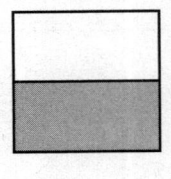

c.

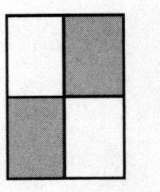

d.

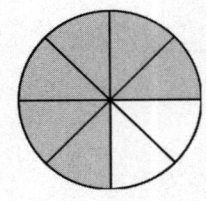

e.

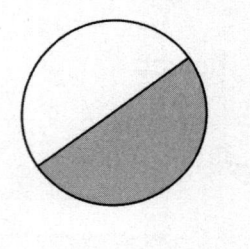

f.

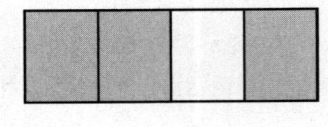

3. Complete the drawing to show 1 whole.

a. This is 1 half.
Draw 1 whole.

b. This is 1 eighth.
Draw 1 whole.

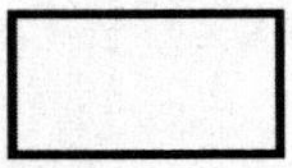

c. This is 1 fourth.
Draw 1 whole.

Name _____   Date _____

What fraction do you need to color so that 1 whole is shaded?

1.

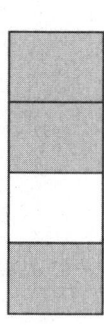

_____

2.

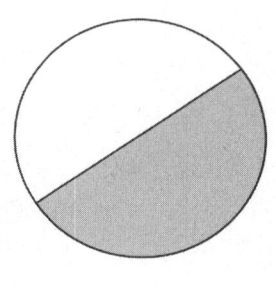

_____

3.

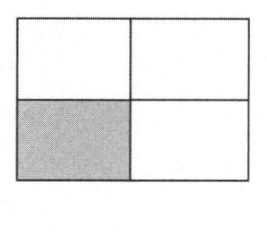

_____

4. What fraction is shaded?

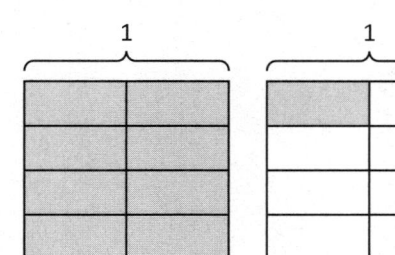

_____

Lesson 11: Use concrete models to count fractional parts beyond one whole.

Name _____ Date _____

1. Tell what fraction of each clock is shaded in the space below using the words *quarter, quarters, half,* or *halves.*

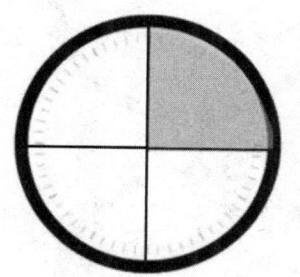

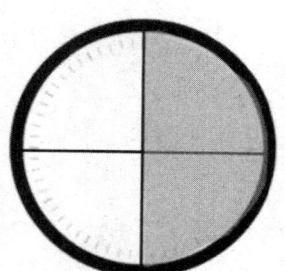

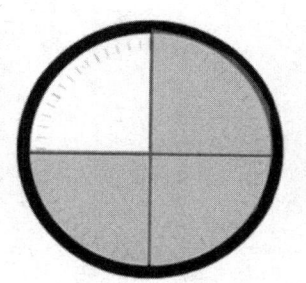

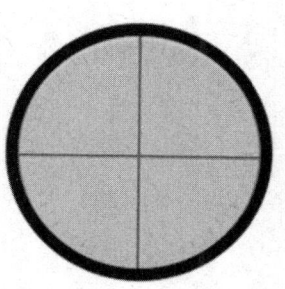

   _____   _____   _____   _____

2. Write the time shown on each clock.

   a.

   _____

   b.

   _____

   c.

   _____

   d.

   _____

3. Match each time to the correct clock by drawing a line.

- Quarter to 4

- Half past 8

- 8:30

- 3:45

- 1:15

3. Draw the minute hand on the clock to show the correct time.

3:45   11:30   6:15

Name _____ Date _____

Draw the minute hand on the clock to show the correct time.

Half past 7   12:15   A quarter to 3

R (Read the problem carefully.)

Brownies take 45 minutes to bake. Pizza takes half an hour less than brownies to warm up. How long does pizza take to warm up?

D (Draw a picture.)

W (Write and solve an equation.)

W (Write a statement that matches the story.)

Name _____ Date _____

1. Fill in the missing numbers.

   60, 55, 50, _____, 40, _____, _____, _____, 20, _____, _____, _____, _____,

2. Fill in the missing numbers on the face of the clock to show the minutes.

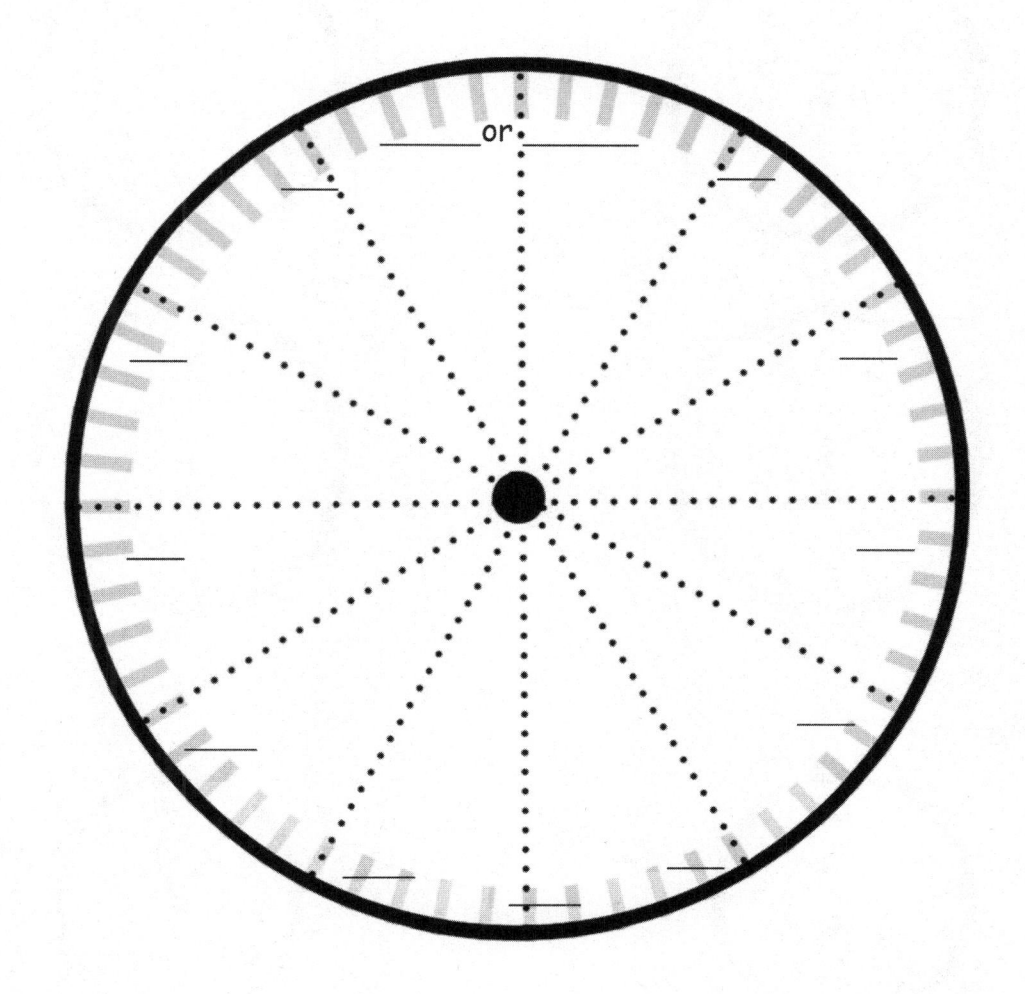

_____ or _____

Lesson 13: Tell time to the nearest five minutes.

3. Draw the hour and minute hands on the clocks to match the correct time.

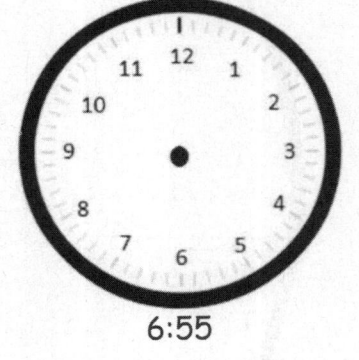

3:05

3:35

4:10

4:40

6:25

6:55

4. What time is it?

_____   _____

Lesson 13: Tell time to the nearest five minutes.

Name _____   Date _____

Draw the hour and minute hands on the clocks to match the correct time.

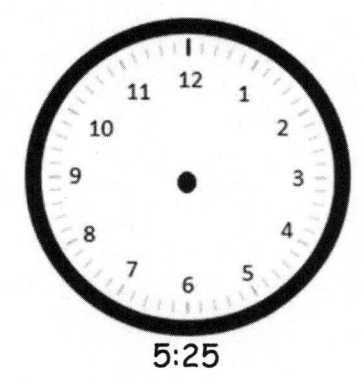

12:55   5:25

Lesson 13: Tell time to the nearest five minutes.

R (Read the problem carefully.)

At Memorial School, students have a quarter hour for morning recess and 33 minutes for a lunch break. How much free time do they have in all? How much more time for lunch than recess do they have?

D (Draw a picture.)

W (Write and solve an equation.)

W (Write a statement that matches the story.)

Name _____   Date _____

1. Decide whether the activity below would happen in the a.m. or the p.m. Circle your answer.

    a. Waking up for school   **a.m. / p.m.**

    b. Eating dinner   **a.m. / p.m.**

    c. Reading a bedtime story   **a.m. / p.m.**

    d. Making breakfast   **a.m. / p.m.**

    e. Having a play date after school   **a.m. / p.m.**

    f. Going to bed   **a.m. / p.m.**

    g. Eating a piece of cake   **a.m. / p.m.**

    h. Eating lunch   **a.m. / p.m.**

Lesson 14: Tell time to the nearest five minutes; relate *a.m.* and *p.m.* to time of day.

2. Draw the hands on the analog clock to match the time on the digital clock. Then, circle **a.m. or p.m.** based on the description given.

   a. Brushing your teeth after you wake up

   7:10   a.m. or p.m.

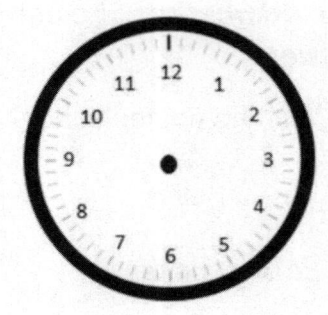

   b. Finishing homework

   5:55   a.m. or p.m.

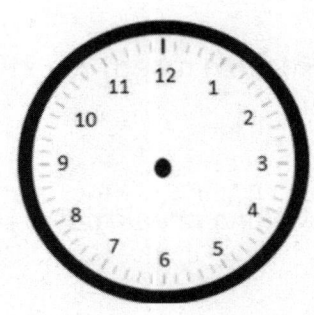

3. Write what you might be doing if it were **a.m.** or **p.m.**

   a. a.m. _____

   b. p.m. _____

4. What time does the clock show?

   ____ : ____

Name _____   Date _____

Draw the hands on the analog clock to match the time on the digital clock. Then, circle **a.m. or p.m.** based on the description given.

1. The sun is rising.

   6:10   a.m. or p.m.

2. Walking the dog

   3:40   a.m. or p.m.

Write the time. Circle a.m. or p.m.

_____ a.m./p.m.

_____
telling time story (large)

Write the time. Circle a.m. or p.m.

_____ a.m./p.m.

_____
telling time story (large)

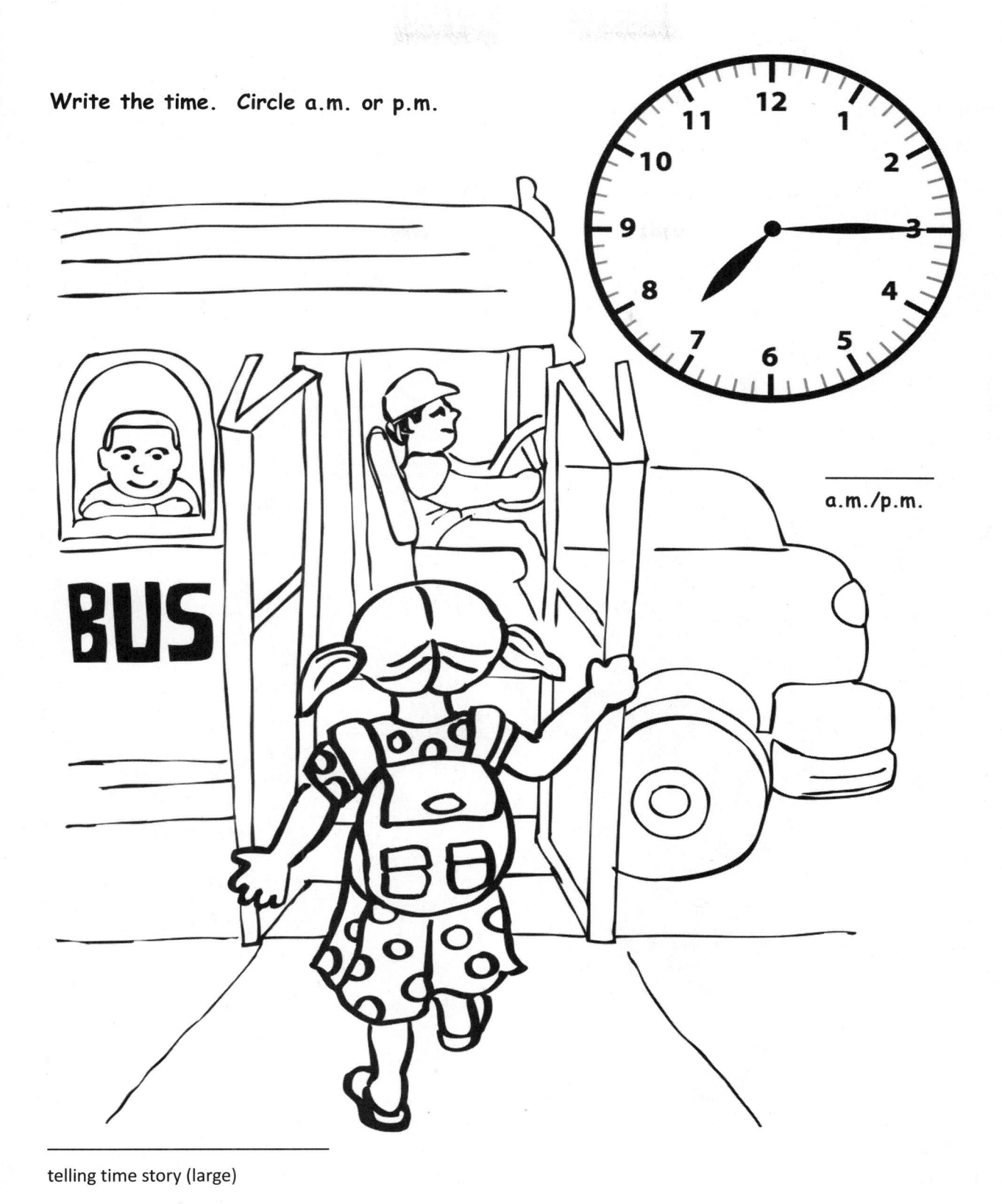

A STORY OF UNITS – TEKS EDITION Lesson 14 Template 2•8

Write the time. Circle a.m. or p.m.

_____
a.m./p.m.

_____
telling time story (large)

Lesson 14: Tell time to the nearest five minutes; relate *a.m.* and *p.m.* to time of day.

95

A STORY OF UNITS – TEKS EDITION

Lesson 14 Template 2•8

Write the time. Circle a.m. or p.m.

_____ a.m./p.m.

telling time story (large)

Lesson 14: Tell time to the nearest five minutes; relate *a.m.* and *p.m.* to time of day.

A STORY OF UNITS – TEKS EDITION Lesson 14 Template 2•8

Write the time. Circle a.m. or p.m.

_____
a.m./p.m.

_____
telling time story (large)

Lesson 14: Tell time to the nearest five minutes; relate *a.m.* and *p.m.* to time of day.

97

A STORY OF UNITS – TEKS EDITION

Lesson 14 Template 2•8

Write the time. Circle a.m. or p.m.

_____ a.m./p.m.

_____
telling time story (large)

Lesson 14: Tell time to the nearest five minutes; relate *a.m.* and *p.m.* to time of day.

Write the time. Circle a.m. or p.m.

_____
a.m./p.m.

_____
telling time story (large)

Lesson 14: Tell time to the nearest five minutes; relate *a.m.* and *p.m.* to time of day.

A STORY OF UNITS – TEKS EDITION

Lesson 14 Template 2•8

Write the time. Circle a.m. or p.m.

_____
a.m./p.m.

_____
telling time story (large)

Lesson 14: Tell time to the nearest five minutes; relate *a.m.* and *p.m.* to time of day.

R (Read the problem carefully.)

Christine has 12 math problems for homework. It takes her 5 minutes to complete each problem. How many minutes does it take Christine to finish all 12 problems?

D (Draw a picture.)

W (Write and solve an equation.)

W (Write a statement that matches the story.)

Name _____   Date _____

1. Follow the directions to label the number line below.

   ←—|—|—|—|—|—|—|—|—|—|—|—|—→

   a. Ingrid gets ready for school between 7:00 a.m. and 8:00 a.m. Label the first and last tick marks as 7:00 a.m. and 8:00 a.m.

   b. Each interval represents 5 minutes. Count by fives starting at 0, or 7:00 a.m. Label each 5-minute interval below the number line up to 8:00 a.m.

   c. Ingrid starts getting dressed at 7:10 a.m. Plot a point on the number line to represent this time. Above the point, write D.

   d. Ingrid starts eating breakfast at 7:35 a.m. Plot a point on the number line to represent this time. Above the point, write E.

   e. Ingrid starts brushing her teeth at 7:40 a.m. Plot a point on the number line to represent this time. Above the point, write T.

   f. Ingrid starts packing her lunch at 7:45 a.m. Plot a point on the number line to represent this time. Above the point, write L.

   g. Ingrid starts waiting for the bus at 7:55 a.m. Plot a point on the number line to represent this time. Above the point, write W.

A STORY OF UNITS – TEKS EDITION

Lesson 15 Problem Set 2•8

2. Label every 5 minutes below the number line shown. Draw a line from each clock to the point on the number line which shows its time. Not all of the clocks have matching points.

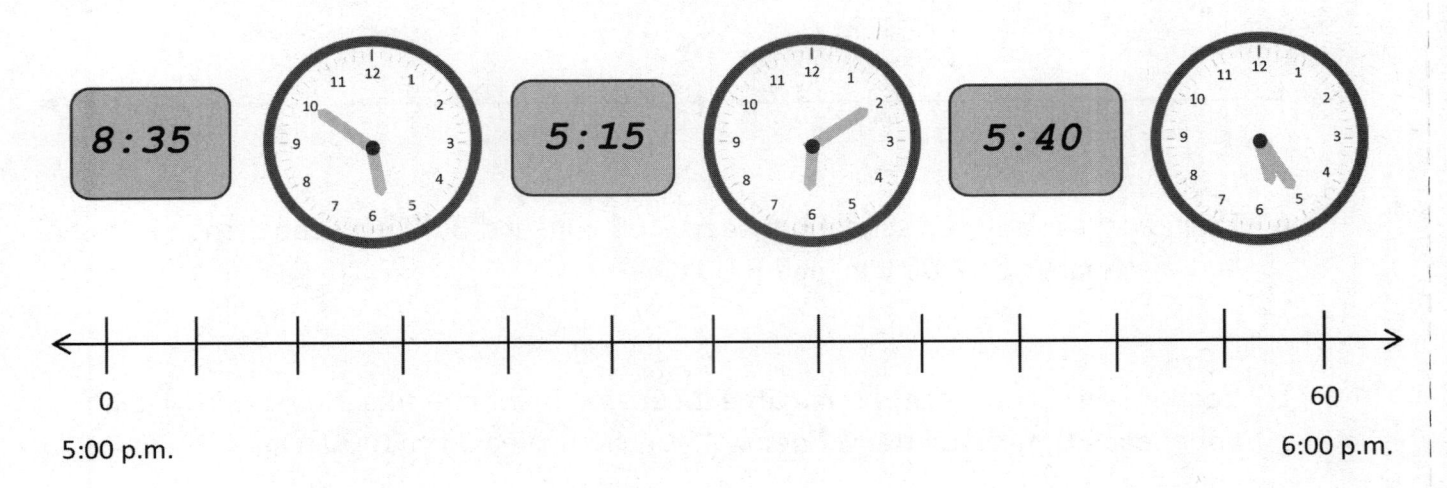

8:35   5:15   5:40

←|————|————|————|————|————|————|————|————|————|————|————|————|→
0   60
5:00 p.m.   6:00 p.m.

3. Noah uses a number line to locate 5:45 p.m. Each interval is 5 minutes. The number line shows the hour from 5 p.m. to 6 p.m. Label the number line below to show his work.

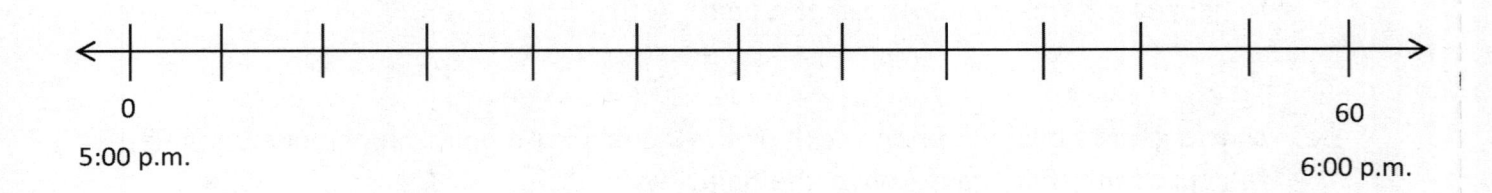

←|————|————|————|————|————|————|————|————|————|————|————|————|→
0   60
5:00 p.m.   6:00 p.m.

4. Tanner tells his little brother that 11:25 p.m. comes after 11:20 a.m. Do you agree with Tanner? Why or why not?

Lesson 15: Relate skip-counting by fives on the clock and telling time to a continuous measurement model, the number line.

Name _____ Date _____

The number line below shows a math class that begins at 10:00 a.m. and ends at 11:00 a.m. Use the number line to answer the following questions.

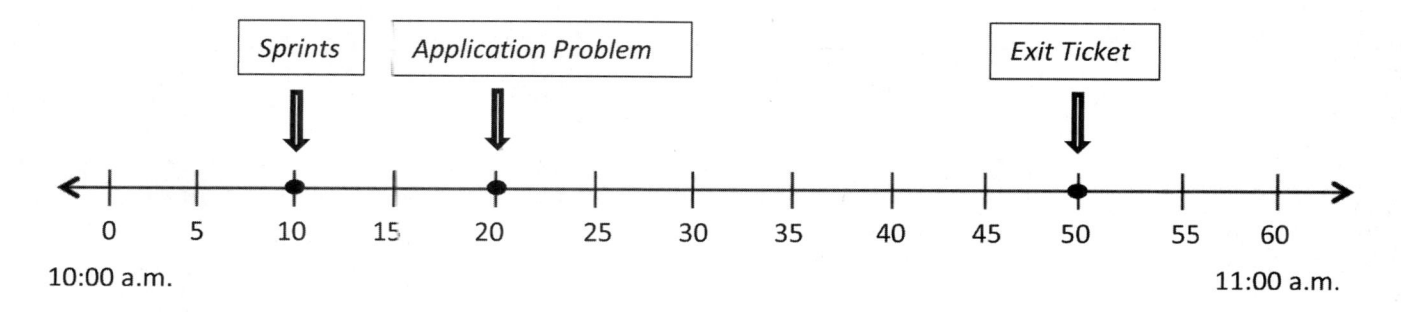

a. What time do Sprints begin?

b. What time do students begin the Application Problem?

c. What time do students work on the Exit Ticket?

d. How long is math class?

strip diagram

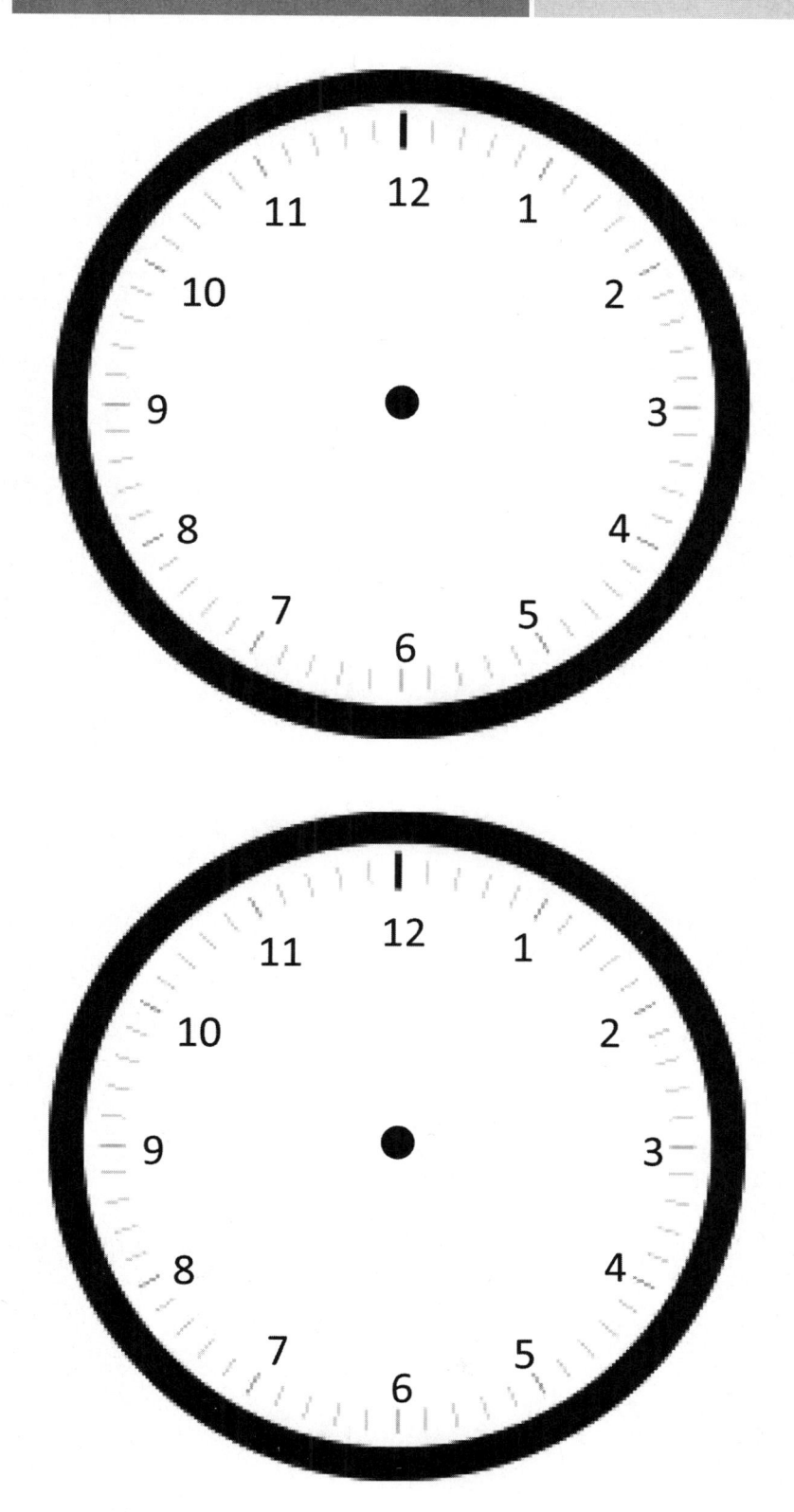

A STORY OF UNITS – TEKS EDITION

Lesson 15 Template 2   2•8

two clocks

Lesson 15: Relate skip-counting by fives on the clock and telling time to a continuous measurement model, the number line.

109

R (Read the problem carefully.)

On Saturdays, Jean may only watch cartoons for one hour. Her first cartoon lasts 14 minutes, and the second lasts 28 minutes. After a 5-minute break, Jean watches a 15-minute cartoon. How much time does Jean spend watching cartoons? Did she break her time limit?

D (Draw a picture.)

W (Write and solve an equation.)

W (Write a statement that matches the story.)

_____

_____

Name _____   Date _____

1. Plot a point on the number line for the times shown on the clocks below. Then, draw a line to match the clocks to the points.

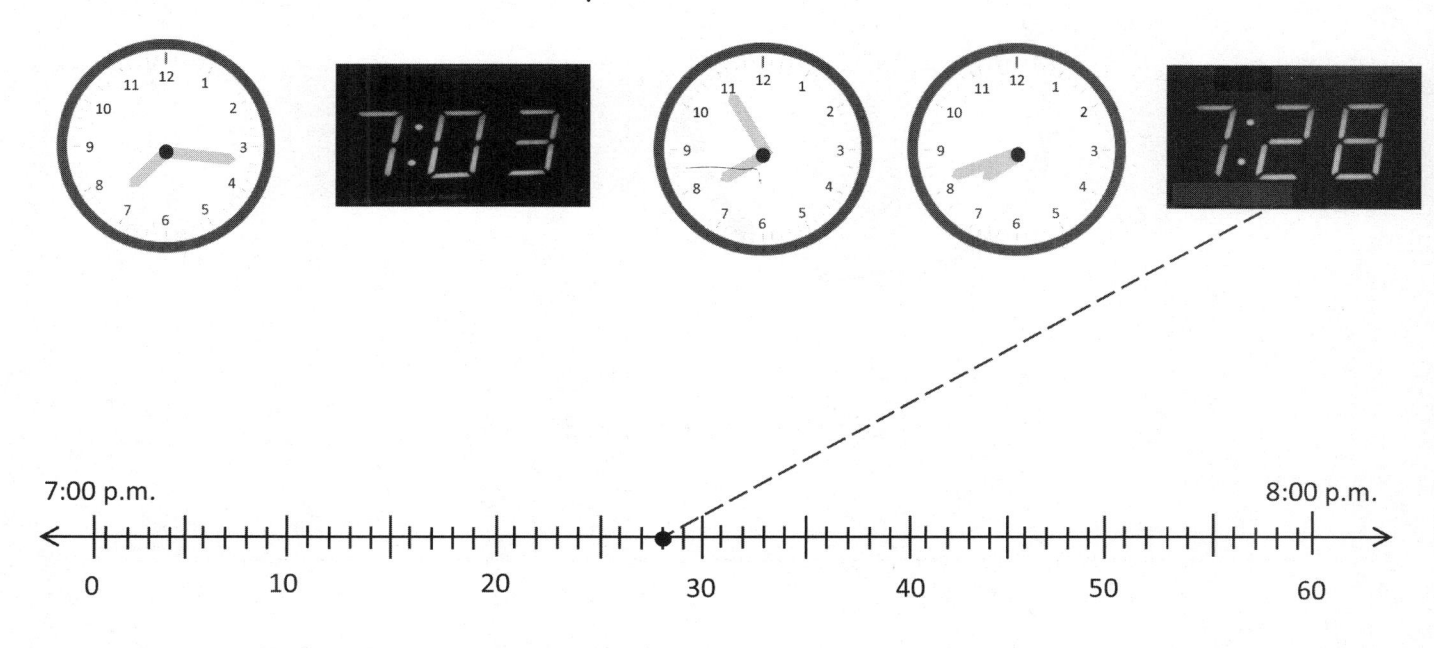

7:00 p.m. ←———————————————————————————→ 8:00 p.m.
           0   10   20   30   40   50   60

2. Jessie woke up this morning at 6:48 a.m. Draw hands on the clock below to show what time Jessie woke up.

3. Mrs. Barnes starts teaching math at 8:23 a.m. Draw hands on the clock below to show what time Mrs. Barnes starts teaching math.

Lesson 16: Count by fives and ones on the number line as a strategy to tell time to the nearest minute on the clock.

4. The clock shows what time Rebecca finishes her homework. What time does Rebecca finish her homework?

Rebecca finishes her homework at _____.

5. The clock below shows what time Mason's mom drops him off for practice.

   a. What time does Mason's mom drop him off?

   b. Mason's coach arrived 11 minutes before Mason. What time did Mason's coach arrive?

Name _____ Date _____

The clock shows what time Jason gets to school in the morning.

Arrival at School

a. What time does Jason get to school?

b. The first bell rings at 8:23 a.m. Draw hands on the clock to show when the first bell rings.

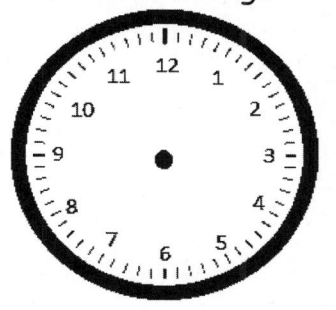

First Bell Rings

c. Label the first and last tick marks 8:00 a.m. and 9:00 a.m. Plot a point to show when Jason arrives at school. Label it A. Plot a point on the line when the first bell rings and label it B.

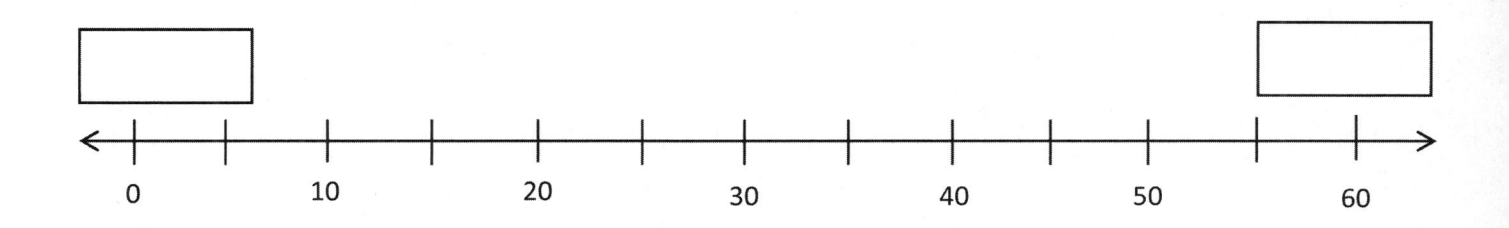

0   10   20   30   40   50   60

Lesson 16: Count by fives and ones on the number line as a strategy to tell time to the nearest minute on the clock.

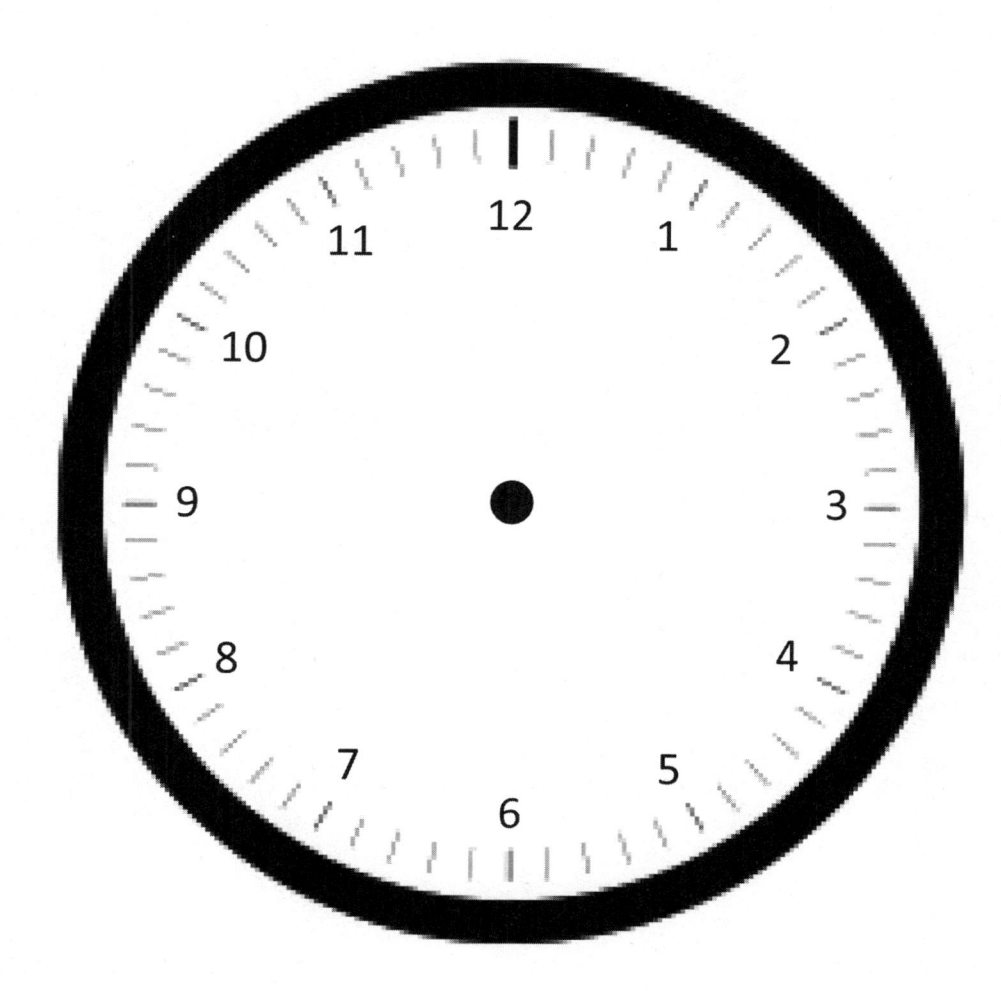

clock

Lesson 16: Count by fives and ones on the number line as a strategy to tell time to the nearest minute on the clock.

Credits

Great Minds® has made every effort to obtain permission for the reprinting of all copyrighted material. If any owner of copyrighted material is not acknowledged herein, please contact Great Minds for proper acknowledgment in all future editions and reprints of this module.